REBEL HEALING

Transforming Ourselves

and the Systems That Make Us Sick

by

NOËLLE JANKA

Publishing Services provided by Paper Raven Books LLC

Printed in the United States of America

First Printing, 2023

Paperback ISBN 979-8-9885040-0-9

Hardback ISBN 979-8-9885040-1-6

TABLE OF CONTENTS

DEDICATION

For Heather Colman-McGill, who often did more for the world in one week with her "tiny energy" than many people achieve in a lifetime.

With deep gratitude to Leslie Salmon Jones and Jeff Jones for lighting the fire of my spiritual healing journey, showing me that healing happens in community, and helping me understand that healing and justice are one.

Free Bonus

Would you like access to step-by-step video demonstrations of the exercises in this book?

Get them FREE here: noellejanka.com/bonus

How to Use this Book

The book is broken up into three sections and there's a glossary of important terms at the end that you can refer to as you read. You have my permission to skip parts or jump around as you feel called. The first section is a set of practices you can start doing right away to shift your experience with pain, illness, and struggle. Doing even some of these practices will help you build a healing foundation that will allow you to get more out of the rest of the book. The second section looks at how our political and social context is making us unwell, and how our dominant culture and institutions contribute to our collective unwellness. It also gets us all on the same page about what healing is, why it matters, and how we can bring a healing lens to our policymaking, our institutions, and our personal relationships. In the third section, I go in greater depth to all my favorite practices and tools for enhancing your mental, emotional, and spiritual well-being, which you can use individually and with others. My hope is that these practices support you to love all parts of yourself and your community more fully, navigate your physical reality with more ease, claim your agency in healing and changemaking, and experience more of the magic of being alive.

Depending on where you are in your healing journey, what you've been exposed to in the healing realm, and how you view and experience the systems that shape our everyday lives, you might find some or a lot of this book unfamiliar. You might find that your brain is quick to judge some of this as too hard, too radical, too mystical, or too unscientific. I would have thought the same about a lot of what I share in this book even a few years ago. Healing requires change, something our brains are wired to resist. Healing requires you to wade through discomfort again and again, and trust that it's taking you somewhere. If some parts of this book ruffle your feathers, feel impossible, or make you so scared you want to shit your pants, you're exactly where you need to be. See if you can approach the material with curiosity and stay with it when discomfort arises. The willingness to persevere in the face of discomfort is a healing practice in itself. That said, if at any point any of the material feels too intense, or you need to switch to something more fun for a while, please put this book down and watch some Queer Eye, pet your cat, do some doodling, talk to a loved one, or listen to a funny podcast. Honor where you are, and please give your nervous system a break if you need it. The second section will be heavy for some people. I've also found that it gets a lot of spoonies really fired up. Regardless, if it feels like too much, you can skip to Section 3 and come back to Section 2. Linearity is overrated anyway!

Since I am white and from a professional class background, I fully expect readers to find ways in which my writing could be more inclusive and intersectional. I strive to be those things, and I am still learning and healing my own internalized oppression. Several people with other identities and perspectives read this book to look out for ableism, racism, and other forms of oppression, but I know we didn't catch it all. I am sorry for any harm this book may cause you or your kin. Please know that I am open to feedback and learning. I can be reached via my website (www.noellejanka.com). I appreciate the courage and emotional labor it can take to name your own pain, and I am so grateful to all the individuals who have helped and will help shape my understanding of what it means to be truly inclusive, accessible, and anti-oppressive. I am also not a social scientist or scholar. I expect readers to find flaws and neglected perspectives in my arguments. If that starts another conversation about healing and justice, I welcome it. I just want more people to talk about this. That is more important to me than being right.

Everything I share in this book is a suggestion, informed by my teachers, and years of experience and experimentation. All the practices and mindset shifts I share have aided me tremendously in my journey and have supported many friends and clients. They certainly aren't the be-all and end-all of healing. The practices offered in this book include a blend of neuroscience, metaphysics, ancient wisdom, and ontology, as well as intuitive, anecdotal, and scientific data. There are more scientific *and* more mystical ways to approach healing, and I encourage you to explore those too, if you feel called to. As much as we'd love to find THE way to heal, there is only YOUR way. The magical thing about the complexity of humans is that there are infinite paths to healing—and you will find yours if you're open to it.

If something in this book doesn't resonate now, it might later on. Sometimes we need to have a certain level of ability or understanding for a particular tool to make sense. It's also not all meant to be done at the same time. I didn't try to put the tools and practices in Section 3 in any particular order because the path is going to be different for everyone. I encourage you to try what resonates with you and leave the rest. Trust that you'll know what you need when you need it. You'll notice that parts of the book are repetitive, and this is by design. Often, we need to hear or read things multiple times before they register, especially if our brains are foggy!

It's also important for me to say that healing is not all about the tools or modalities you pursue. Healing is a mindset, a process, and a practice. Part of why my healing journey has been so arduous is that I was, and continue to be at times, very hard on myself. The only reason I'm still here is because I committed to loving myself, even when I didn't really understand what that would entail. I encourage you to be patient and gentle with yourself and trust your own brilliance and intuition.

If you read nothing else in this book, read Healing Principles and the Cultivate Self-Love in Section 3. Learning to love yourself is like the glue that holds the whole healing ship together. It's also what allows you to really show up for others with compassion. Not being able to love our wholeness—our beauty, our mess, and everything in between—is the basis of all human suffering, chronic illness included. That applies on individual and collective levels. If everyone had the support they needed to truly love all of themselves, we probably wouldn't have as many mass shootings, family abuse, or so many entities that value profit over the earth and human lives. Committing to loving yourself, your body included, is one of the best things you can do for yourself and everyone around you. When you can see your messiness clearly *and* accept it, rather than getting tangled up in it, it frees up your energy for other things, like pursuing what is most important to you, and acting in alignment with your deepest values. That, in turn, allows you to be more present for others and gives you more energy to contribute to those around you.

We can experience liberation when we see the wholeness of the collective as well. By understanding that our society has the capacity to uproot our racism, sexism, ableism, homophobia, patriarchy, white supremacy, and other patterns of domination, we can begin to see each other as humans again. We can reclaim our humanity, which we need to fully dismantle systems of oppression, heal from health challenges, and build something new that will support all of our well-being. Loving the collective is a lot easier when you are on a self-love journey yourself.

Your paths of healing and self-love might lead in unexpected directions and precipitate some big leaps out of your comfort zone. I met a former scientist recovering from Lyme disease who, in the process of healing, discovered she was able to communicate with dead people and animals. I witnessed her work and she's very gifted. Helping people talk to their dead kitties is definitely not something her pre-healing-journey self would have expected. As you travel on your healing path, my number one recommendation is to stay open to what my friend Mattie once called, "The infinite possibilities of being a human being." Do that, and victory will find you.

INTRODUCTION

I have been sick and/or in pain for most of my adult life, but this book isn't really about me. This book is a love letter, a self-help guide, and a community empowerment tool for individuals living with health challenges. It is a guide to the mental, emotional, and spiritual aspects of healing personally and collectively—essentially all the good stuff you don't get in the doctor's office. Because of this psycho-spiritual focus, the book may also be useful to individuals who are not explicitly experiencing health challenges but may be struggling with related challenges of addiction, grief, mental health, and/or trauma recovery.

Why "Rebel Healing?" This is not like any other book you've read about healing. This is the book I wish I'd had earlier in my healing journey. The book I needed when I felt like no one could help me and I turned my pain back on myself. It took me years to see myself in the larger web of unwellness in this country, as well as the web of collective movements for healing. Eventually I learned that when we see our illness in context, it becomes clear that we need to act in non-normative or rebellious ways in order to heal. I wanted to create a guide that allows people to see that their illness is not their fault, and that they have tremendous agency in healing both themselves *and* the systems that made them sick. As a trained grassroots organizer and politicized life and career coach, I am always thinking about our relationships with the political and cultural systems in which we are living. With this lens, I explore how we can heal *within* the context that made us unwell in the first place, and how our healing can be both a political act and a contribution to the collective. My own experience with illness is what forced me out of doing political work as an organizer and led me to become a coach for social impact and social movement leaders. It became clear to me that my role is to be a healer and only by honoring that calling would I start to experience more ease in my life. Like me, many of my clients have struggled with burnout and health challenges. In my own experience and my clients', I've seen many opportunities to avoid struggle by reframing the interconnectedness of healing and justice and the way we approach both processes. I wanted this book to both contextualize our collective illness and provide a roadmap to navigating the paths of healing and justice at the same time, in community.

While there are many, many books on how to heal—physically, emotionally, spiritually, sexually, and otherwise—in my own healing journey I struggled to find books that addressed both why we are sick *and* how to heal inside a toxic society. Since I started writing this manuscript, a flurry of new books has come out that explore these questions. To my knowledge, at this time, the only other book that explores these themes together through the lens of chronic health challenges is Dr. Gabor Maté's *The Myth of Normal: Trauma, Illness, and Healing in a Toxic Culture*, which came out in September 2022. It's an amazing book, and different in that it's more scientific and not as collectively oriented. I have included a list of recent related books in the appendix, as well as older ones I found helpful in exploring these questions.

How do healing and justice fit together? Bryan Stevenson, criminal justice reform advocate and founder of the Equal Justice Initiative has said that "The opposite of poverty is not wealth. The opposite of poverty is justice." In that vein, this book argues that the opposite of illness is not health, but justice. Our unhealthiness as individuals is not the issue. The issue is that our unjust systems make us unhealthy. Despite spending more on healthcare than any other country in the world, the U.S. has some of the poorest health outcomes. More than sixty percent of Americans have at least one chronic health condition, and that figure doesn't include autoimmune disease, Lyme disease, myalgic encephalomyelitis, long COVID, and other debilitating conditions that affect huge swaths of the population. The Centers for Disease Control and Prevention tells us that the leading causes of chronic disease are tobacco and alcohol use, poor nutrition, and lack of physical activity. I have tons of chronically ill friends. Most of them exercise, all of them eat extremely healthily, and none of them use alcohol or tobacco. This country's propensity to dump all the onus on the individual obscures the oppressive systems that are making us sick, gaslighting and victim blaming the millions who experience chronic illness. Yes, we have an individual responsibility to take care of ourselves, and yes, we have agency in our own healing. We also have agency in changing the systems that make us sick. But in order to facilitate healing and change, we need to understand the actual causes of chronic disease in this country:

1. The myth of individualism
2. Systemic oppression[1] in our schools, governments, healthcare system, culture, etc.
3. The resulting trauma, disconnection, and isolation experienced by individuals and communities
4. Societal programming we've internalized that reinforces systemic oppression and the myth of individualism and makes it more challenging to connect to our own truths

---

1 This is systemic oppression rooted in white supremacy, racism, patriarchy, colonialism, ableism, homophobia, transphobia, and the U.S.'s particular brand of underregulated capitalism.

Though these causes of chronic disease may feel intractable, they can be healed, personally and collectively. On the personal level, once you can recognize how these forces show up in your life, you have the opportunity to choose how you relate to them. Once you take back some of your agency, it becomes easier to discern what in your belief system is social programming or trauma versus what is true for you—and make your life choices accordingly. After practicing this myself and supporting hundreds of others with this healing process through my work as a coach, I can say with confidence that this discernment process is some of the most important medicine for changing your experience with chronic health challenges.

On the collective level, as more people do their own healing work, expand their capacity for connection, and trade individualism for interdependence, we will have a much greater capacity to change the oppressive systems that keep all of us, and especially the most marginalized, from being free. Because healing trauma requires safety, some traumatized individuals will not be able to heal fully until our *systems* have healed and changed. I think this means that those of us with multiple levels of privilege, who don't live in constant danger, have a moral obligation to heal the oppression that lives within us and direct some of our gifts, energy, and attention to making it more possible for others in our communities to heal. As life becomes more dangerous for all of us in the face of climate disaster, pandemics, loss of abortion rights, gun violence, and other escalating threats, it is critical that we both grieve and heal together, and resource each other as we're able. Writer, performer, and cultural worker Kai Cheng Thom has written that collective "healing" in many cases means preparing our bodies to survive and "experience joy in the face of great danger."[2]

Depending on where you are in your healing journey, the identities that you hold, and your own experience with systemic oppression, this book's discussion of political context may feel familiar or very new. My

2 Kai Cheng Thom, Twitter post, August 2019, https://twtext.com/article/1159287304789405699#

suspicion is that for many readers, the tension between mainstream healing messaging and what we actually experience in day-to-day reality is something you've felt in your bones but perhaps haven't had many opportunities to discuss and interrogate. If it's very familiar, I hope you can use the book to help others grow in their understanding of our context. If the politics of healing is a newer exploration for you, I hope you'll take advantage of the journal prompts in the book to help you process. And, if you are able, I strongly suggest you read this book with others so you can discuss what it brings up for you and work on healing together.

When I speak about healing in this book, I am primarily referring to the mental, emotional, and spiritual work we need to do to move through the world as our most authentic, connected selves. This work is critical in supporting a body to heal itself. This is also the work that will support all of us to build systems and communities that are healing rather than harming. What you won't find in this book is advice on what to eat, what supplements to take, physical exercises, or how to fix your sleep. There are a million other books on that stuff. I personally found that I could not achieve my own healing goals by working with the body alone. All the yoga, diet changes, supplements, and healing protocols just didn't get me very far. Conversely, when I started cultivating spiritual connection, healing trauma, listening to my body, unlearning oppressive social programming, and leaning into community support, I started experiencing significant breakthroughs with my physical symptoms. I don't like promising certain results when it comes to healing, because everyone's path will be different. What I can promise is that if you adopt some of the healing framework and practices outlined in this book, and stick with them for a while, you will move through the world with more ease, grace, satisfaction, connection, and joy.

Here are some themes we'll explore:
- What healing is and how you get to define what it means to you.
- Why understanding the social and political context that initiated your illness is important.
- How many so-called "chronic" illnesses are only chronic because the medical system does not understand them or doesn't care to understand them.
- Some history on why the American medical system is f-ed because white guys took it over in the nineteenth century, shunned traditional healing methods, shut out experienced healers (read: women and/or Black and Indigenous healers), and monetized health for profit.
- How the medical system continues to fail us because we have not uprooted white supremacy, capitalism, patriarchy, ableism, transphobia in which our medical system is steeped.
- How healing is a community affair. This book looks at what it means to heal in community even if you don't talk to your family and feel like you don't have any friends.
- How everything is always personal and collective. Your suffering and your healing are never just yours. The only way we will significantly shift health outcomes in this country, eradicate white supremacy, and survive the climate apocalypse is by doing our own healing and healing in community with others.
- How to heal the oppression that lives within us so that we can build systems that are healing instead of harming.
- How your challenges and commitment to healing can be a superpower.

Why should you trust *me* to teach you anything about healing?
Here's a little about me and why I took the time to birth this book

baby.[3] I am a coach and a yoga teacher, and I've had the privilege of supporting hundreds of mission-driven individuals with their healing in the last seven years, with a specific focus on healing internalized capitalism and other imprints of oppression, domination, and trauma. Many of the folks I work with are fellow chronic illness survivors. I've been living with chronic illness myself for more than twenty years. When I was 15, I started experiencing symptoms of what was eventually diagnosed as Chronic Inflammatory Response Syndrome (CIRS), Lyme disease, bartonella, babesia, and mycoplasma. I personally have no memory of it, but my mom remembers that I got a bad "flu," was out for a few days, and then all kinds of weird symptoms emerged after that. My knees hurt a lot. I had trouble reading without my eyes getting blurry and fatigued, despite having 20/20 vision. I had ulcers and got tired easily. I had shooting pains and a lot of muscle twitches throughout my whole body. My doctors said I had chronic fatigue syndrome and told me to take prenatal vitamins. Despite living in a Lyme endemic area, I was not tested. Lingering Epstein-Barr Virus was also not addressed. When I returned to the doctor with more symptoms, they said I was too stressed. It didn't seem normal to me to be so tired, creaky, and unable to read at my age, but I accepted that as my body's normal for a long time, until I couldn't anymore.

Over the years more symptoms appeared, like issues with memory recall, brain fog, migraines, mood swings, digestive challenges, a heart condition, dysautonomia, and all kinds of body pain that didn't respond to massage, physical therapy, acupuncture, pain killers, or anything else. I was cold all the time, never sweated, and couldn't produce a fever. I spent many years feeling like I didn't want to be alive. I would walk to work daydreaming about how nice it might be to step out into traffic and have it all be over. (Sorry, Mom.) Every day was so hard. I didn't see the point. It was a sucky way to live.

---

3 I know sometimes reading about other people's illnesses is triggering. I have put many books down halfway through the intro because I didn't want to read about the author's horrifying medical trauma. Please know you have my full permission to skip these four paragraphs!

Some doctors and researchers will tell you that "late-stage," "chronic," or "post-treatment" Lyme disease isn't real. Many people who contract Lyme and/or other tick-borne illnesses, if treated early, can take antibiotics and experience a full recovery, but an estimated 10-20% of cases remain unresolved after 24 months.[4] I was sick for nearly a decade before getting diagnosed. When I finally did take antibiotics, they didn't make a huge difference, and in some ways made me sicker.

For most of my adult life until recently, I was pretty sure I'd always be sick or in pain or both. I went through a boom and bust cycle of feeling really bad and feeling well enough, at times accepting a fibromyalgia diagnosis I was given in my 20s, and at other times searching desperately for another possible answer. In 2012, after getting a concussion in a bike crash, my symptoms surged and I recommitted to getting to the bottom of the illness. But even after receiving a Lyme diagnosis that year, things got worse before they got better. I had to learn how to hold the dream that I could be pain- and disease-free while also accepting that those things were, and could always be, part of my day-to-day reality. I decided I would try to figure out how to live the best life I could, even if I was going to feel sick and in pain everyday. I did eventually experience a period of about nine months in which I felt nearly 100%. I had a small relapse shortly before we all went into quarantine for COVID and like many folks with health challenges, the stress of the pandemic increased my fatigue. Still, I was so much better than I had been for many years. Then I got the Johnson & Johnson COVID vaccine in April 2021, and it felt like getting a concussion all over again. I experienced panic attacks, started crashing into things, and in the ensuing months almost all the past symptoms returned, some worse than ever before. It has been an opportunity to put all my healing knowledge into practice again and heal on a deeper level.

---

4 "Lyme Disease Facts and Statistics," Bay Area Lyme Foundation, July 21, 2022, https://www.bayarealyme.org/about-lyme/lyme-disease-facts-statistics/.

Except for a few very helpful surgeries and one miracle medication, allopathic medicine[5] has not done that much for me. After years and years of letdowns, I decided I'd have to figure out how to heal without that support. In my research, I became interested in the question of why some folks get sick and stay sick.

What was the difference in causation, and why were some folks able to heal fully from Lyme[6], MS, Chronic Fatigue Syndrome, and Fibromyalgia, while others remained sick their whole lives?

Holding these questions in my heart, I became an eager student of healing, investing a lot of time, energy, and money into figuring out what it really takes for a person to heal. I spent countless hours reading and listening to personal accounts of people who, after finding no answers or unsatisfactory answers in the mainstream medical system, took healing matters into their own hands.

I met people who had completely reversed decades of debilitating depression, anxiety, and multiple chemical sensitivities after doing a brain retraining program called the Dynamic Neural Retraining System. I talked to others who shared accounts of healing fully through meditation, cultivating self-love, saying affirmations, and talking to angels. I also met people who worked with a variety of mainstream and alternative doctors and healers until they finally found a combination of medicines that shifted things for them.

I was filled with hope seeing these former sick people move through the world with ease, vitality oozing out of their eyeballs. I was moved to see how they could contribute tremendously to the lives of others from a place of fullness.

5 "Allopathic medicine refers to a system in which medical doctors and other healthcare professionals (such as nurses, pharmacists, and therapists) treat symptoms and diseases using drugs, radiation, or surgery. Also called bio-medicine, conventional medicine, mainstream medicine, orthodox medicine, and Western medicine." ""Allopathic and Osteopathic Medicine," Columbia College and Columbia Engineering, accessed November 20, 2021, https://www.cc-seas.columbia.edu/preprofessional/health/types/allopathic.php.

6 I could have written a whole book about Lyme and CIRS and my experience with them but I didn't want to. I wanted to write about chronic illness more broadly, as informed by my experience, the experience of my clients, and my chronic illness community, because there is so much overlap between us—both in how we get sick and what it takes to heal. If you want to read more about Lyme specifically, Pamela Weintraub, Katina Makris, Dr. Richard Horowitz, Wolf Storl, Stephen Harrod Buhner, Dr. Neil Nathan (also great on mold), and many others have written informative, inspiring, and very practical books on the topic.

In talking to all those people about healing, I got a lot of recommendations, and I tried a lot of different approaches to physical healing. I also got into spiritual and emotional healing work and did everything I could to orient my energy and attention towards healing—what I call adopting a healing mindset. As much as I wanted to give up and die for a very long time, I also really wanted life to feel easier, and I continued to collect evidence that that was possible.

Soon after I got diagnosed with Lyme, I met a fellow patient who looked me in the eye and said, "You are going to get better." We were both sick at the time but something about the conviction in her voice made me believe her. She was right. I still have tick borne infections and Epstein-Barr Virus in my system, and my digestive system remains compromised from taking so many antibiotics, but today I experience way less pain (physical and emotional) than I used to, and I'm truly thrilled to be alive.

Navigating my day-to-day can still feel hard, I'm still tired and feel faint often, but life's a million times sweeter and more fun than it used to be. My relationships are deeper and more satisfying, and I'm able to do a lot more with limited energy because I'm not so emotionally bogged down by my physical symptoms. I'm no longer comparing myself to more able-bodied people and feeling despair about what I cannot do. My healing experience also led me to coaching and becoming a coach, a role I love and appreciate everyday.

Who is this book for?

While many of the lessons in it will be useful to people healing from other types of suffering, I wrote this book for people with chronic health challenges. Chronic illness by definition cannot be cured. That said, there is so much opportunity for us to have different relationships with our physical experience and I wanted more folks to know now what it took me years to learn: you can be in pain without suffering.

You can live in a super unpredictable, conventionally inconvenient body, and still have a wonderful life.

This book is for everyone who has been dismissed in the doctor's office, everyone who has had to see way too many doctors to get a diagnosis, and everyone who does not have a diagnosis or doesn't resonate with diagnoses they've been given. I'm writing this book with Lyme disease, fibromyalgia, ME/CFS, autoimmune disease, long COVID, and similar lesser understood invisible illnesses in mind because they are what I'm most familiar with. I suspect someone with a more widely studied, inherited, or acquired chronic condition or illness might also get something out of this book. If that's you and you decide to read this book, I'd love to hear what you think.

In this book I use the term "spoonie" to encompass anyone who, because of chronic illness, chronic pain, and/or another physical and/or mental health challenge, possesses less physical and emotional energy than the average able-bodied person. The term "spoonie" grew out of a blog post titled "Spoon Theory" by lupus survivor and early chronic illness blogger Christine Miserandino.[7] In trying to explain to her friend what it was like to have a chronic illness while they ate together in a diner, she likened her limited energy to having only a certain number of spoons each day. An able-bodied person might come into any given day with 12 spoons worth of energy, while someone with chronic illness might come into the day with six. If they want to do the laundry, that takes two spoons. Then they must be very judicious about how they use their remaining four spoons. If they want to eat, for example, preparing food might take the rest of their spoons, leaving no spoons for working, going to the store, visiting with a friend, or doing anything else.

I like the term spoonie because it unifies people across all different kinds of health challenges. I also like that saying I'm a spoonie allows

7 Christine Miserandino, "The Spoon Theory," But You Don't Look Sick? support for those with invisible illness or chronic illness, April 26, 2013, https://butyoudontlooksick.com/articles/written-by-christine/the-spoon-theory/.

me to acknowledge that health challenges are a part of my life without talking about a particular diagnosis or symptoms. I have found it useful to teach my loved ones about Spoon Theory so they can ask me, "How's your spoon count?" or "Do you have the spoons for this right now?" It's a nice way to be acknowledged, seen, and supported without having to go into any detail about how I'm feeling. I can be real without giving my challenges too much attention. There are some really nice spoonie communities out there on the internet and they provide a convenient way to connect with folks who have a shared experience, especially if you're house or bed bound. That said, some online chronic illness forums can feel like an endless pit of despair, so know what you're getting into and be discerning about which communities feel supportive to you. I talk more about building a community of people who "get it" in Build a Support Dream Team, in Section 3. Some people find it more useful to eschew all descriptions of illness and how they're feeling, including Spoon Theory, and I respect that.

I'm writing this book for folks in the United States specifically because I believe our culture, healthcare system, and other institutions are set up in ways that contribute to and exacerbate inequality and poor health outcomes, and I wanted to speak to that specifically. The U.S. lens of this book doesn't mean that you won't get anything out of it if you live elsewhere. A lot of the healing practices I recommend can be practiced anywhere in the world. However, one of my arguments is that context matters and I want people with chronic illness in this country to understand where they fit in the current health crisis here in the United States.

I'm also writing this book for readers who, like my coaching clients, feel things deeply and can't help but want to correct the injustices in the world. The inclination to correct injustice, if not done thoughtfully and in right-relationship (to our bodies, the earth, and other beings) can cause harm at the personal and collective level. This book is written to support readers in making change from a more healed and connected place.

If you haven't heard it yet, let me be the one to tell you that you can and will heal. I don't care what your doctors and other people in your life have told you. Even if you always have pain or other physical limitations, you can still live an awesome life. Things can and will get better than they are now. And my hope is that, with the practices outlined in this book, you might get there with more ease than I did. The upside of me being sick for so long is that I have had a lot of time to gather up wisdom. I've been through the ringer a few times, and I've learned a lot along the way. I've experienced abuse, neglect, and sexism in the American healthcare system. I've also spent time with and supported *a lot* of other sick folks and people who are healing.

Some folks who are sick are not interested in healing, and that's okay. Others are simply too sick to do anything other than exist. They are still beautiful and worthy of our care, love, and attention. Most people who eventually do get on the healing path need to really wallow in the shitty parts of being sick for a while before they commit to healing. Especially for folks who acquire illness as adults, there is usually a lot of crying, kicking, screaming, and grieving that happens before healing can start. That's common and a healthy part of the process. The phase after wallowing is acceptance. It involves accepting that you are sick, and that at least in the immediate future, you need to care for yourself as someone with a health condition. Once you accept what is, then all of you can begin to heal with more ease.

As a coach, I can only support people who have reached a certain level of acceptance and are willing to get a little more uncomfortable in the service of their healing. In my personal life, I've also spent a lot of time with sick people who aren't or aren't yet on the healing path—in support groups, at courses and conferences, and through providing peer support. If I had gotten paid for all the time I've spent counseling fellow Lyme patients, I'd probably have a sweet little nest egg now. I am grateful that I've been able to give back to my community. I just point this out to illustrate how much time we need to give each other, especially when we have diseases that the mainstream healthcare system largely refuses to understand. Given that there is no established cure for Lyme[8] and that it can show up so differently in different people, healing Lyme disease can feel like shooting in the dark. The only way any of us have gotten better is with the support and counsel of other survivors who told us which doctors to see and not see, what to believe and not to believe in the literature, and what it actually takes to feel better. I'm enormously grateful to everyone who has counseled me and cried with me on my journey. Nearly everything I've done to heal has been recommended to me by another spoonie. I'll say it many more times in this book, but healing is not something we can do alone—so come on in and get as comfy as you can. Wherever you are in your healing journey, even if you haven't started yet, you are welcome at this party.

---

8 That is, other than hyperthermia which is not available in the United States. Hyperthermia treatment is a carefully administered process in which the temperature of your body is increased to a very high heat that will kill the bacteria associated with Lyme disease. It is also sometimes used to kill cancerous tumors.

SECTION 1

BUILDING A STRONG FOUNDATION

Now that you have a sense of how you can use this book and we've reviewed some shared definitions, I want to begin to offer some practices and exercises to support you with the emotional, cognitive, and spiritual aspects of healing health challenges. The idea is to get your mind, heart, and spirit on board to heal the body on a deeper level. This material will give your body some support so it's not doing this healing thing all by its lonesome. I'll also suggest ways that you can bring other people into your healing process, for your own benefit and theirs.

I want to invite you to define for yourself what healing looks like for you. When I say "heal" in the personal sense, I'm not talking about achieving a state of health in body or mind in which everything is 100% and you experience no pain, discomfort, or limitation. Not only is that impossible, because to be human is to suffer, but you might also have a condition, or conditions, that you will have for the rest of your life. *And* having a truly permanent health challenge does not preclude you from experiencing great healing. Healing is a holistic affair that involves all parts of your being. Even if you don't experience a change in physical symptoms, by committing to healing you might find that you can experience more ease, joy, and satisfaction. You might find yourself with a whole new outlook on life, yourself, and the world. I encourage you to be open to surprises. I talk about community a lot in this book because healing is not something you can do alone. Don't even try. If asking for help and building relationships are things you struggle with, keep breathing. I see you and I've got you. We'll walk through it together.

I highly recommend getting a notebook or starting a document on one of your devices to serve as your healing journal as you work through this book. If writing isn't accessible but you can speak, you might try talk-to-text, which is available in Google Docs. This will allow you to keep your answers to the reflection questions in one place. You can also use your healing journal as a place to record any ideas or observations you have as you read this book and try out the recommended practices.

The third section of this book is where we'll really get into the HOW of healing but I want to give you some foundational practices right off the bat. I picked these because they save energy, regulate your nervous system, increase clarity, and spark joy. Starting with these and practicing them consistently will allow you to do some of the deeper work with more ease. These practices are simple and I offer different options and modifications. If you are already acquainted with any of these practices, I want to invite you to approach them with a beginner's mind[1] and see if there is anything new to learn or experience. I also want to invite you to revisit practices you may have previously written off. Just because something didn't work for you three years ago doesn't

---

1 Beginner's Mind "refers to having an attitude of openness, eagerness, and lack of preconceptions when studying, even at an advanced level, just as a beginner would." "Shoshin," Wikipedia, December 18, 2022, https://en.wikipedia.org/wiki/Shoshin.

mean it won't be a game changer this time around. I suggest this only because I found it to be true in my own journey.

You can think of developing these foundational practices as a cross between knitting yourself a baby blanket and starting an intense fitness regimen. You're going to show your inner child and reptilian brain that they are safe and in good hands so that you can build up your mental and spiritual resiliency. This combo will help you stay calmer, happier, and more able to ride the rollercoaster of healing with more ease. Even if you get to a point when you feel a million times better than you do today—and I hope you do—suffering of some kind is a guarantee, because that's just part of being alive. In some ways, health challenges can feel harder once they've become less severe because then every little thing that pops up can seem like a setback. It's okay to feel sad and frustrated, and making space to feel those feelings is important. But, the more easily you can roll with the punches without letting them keep you down too long, the more energy you'll have to actually live your life and heal. You'll still feel the pain of the punches, but they won't stop you in your tracks in the same way. If you do nothing other than what's in this section, you will already have an easier time going forward.

Six Steps to Building a Strong Foundation for Healing:
1. Make friends with your nervous system
2. Make your life easier
3. Maintain a mindfulness practice
4. Write a vision statement for your healing journey
5. Cultivate a mindset of gratitude and abundance
6. Pursue joy and pleasure

Starting with these steps now will help you get more out of the rest of the book. They're aimed at grounding your nervous system and opening your mind to the journey ahead. This is also me letting you dip your toe in the water before I push you off the high dive later. Just kidding! I'm not going to do that, but I will tell you that healing can require tremendous growth, and often that's uncomfortable. Sometimes we don't wanna. So I'm trying to set you up for success here. The growth is going to feel much more manageable if you're already strengthening your core (the core of your being) with these practices.

If these steps sound basic to you and you feel like you've got them covered, you have my full permission to jump to Section 2!

These foundational practices that calm and fortify the mind and spirit will complement and bring ease to any healing work you do for your body—like shifting to an anti-inflammatory diet, developing a new exercise routine, strengthening your immune system, etc. Okay. Let's begin!

Step 1: Make Friends with Your Nervous System

Here we'll look together at what the nervous system is and why understanding how it works is so important to healing physically and otherwise. I'll offer practices you can use to regulate your own nervous system, and exercises for harmonizing multiple nervous systems in group gatherings. This basic introduction is intended to support you in building awareness of the state of your own nervous system so you can experience more ease in your day-to-day life and make more informed decisions about what healing paths are going to be most supportive for you.

In the last few decades, more researchers and healing practitioners have come to understand that the root cause of many chronic health and mental health conditions is nervous system dysregulation caused by acute trauma, complex trauma, and/or chronic stress. Merriam-Webster defines dysregulation as "impairment of a physiological regulatory mechanism (as that governing metabolism, immune response, or organ function)." We have known for a long time that stress causes illness, and now we are starting to improve our understanding of why. In this chapter we'll look specifically at the autonomic nervous system (ANS), which regulates our stress response, and many other bodily functions like heart rate, digestion, and our ability to relate to others around us. The ANS is responsible for a lot, which is why when it's not working properly it can throw off multiple bodily functions and create a long list of seemingly unrelated symptoms. And, as we learn more about the connection between the ANS and chronic health and mental health challenges, we are also learning more about how to get the ANS back in working order.

One way we can better understand the ANS and the stress response is to learn the basics of Polyvagal Theory. Neuroscientist Stephen Porges developed Polyvagal Theory in 1994 to explain how the cranial nerves produce specific physiological responses in the body.[2] It is a "theory" because it is not yet fully supported by empirical, scientific research. That said, by providing a different understanding of how trauma affects our physiology and how our physiology can be manipulated, Polyvagal Theory has helped therapists, bodyworkers, doctors, and patients around the world achieve previously unattainable healing results with their patients. Polyvagal Theory has provided me with a very useful framework for understanding what is happening in my body and how I can work *with* it. It's also supported me to better understand my clients' experiences. I'm going to give a brief overview of the ANS and Polyvagal Theory here but you can find a more technical explanation, complete with visuals, in the Appendix.

Many people are familiar with the term fight or flight. We know that being in a chronic state of fight/flight means our nervous system is working on overdrive—making it hard to connect with others, ourselves, and putting us at higher risk for chronic physical and mental health challenges. Fight/flight, a state of attacking or feeling in response to fear, is one of the three primary physiological states of the ANS, along with social engagement and shutdown/collapse. There are also three hybrid states: freeze, play, and stillness. Social engagement is the state we're in when we feel safe enough to be social. This is the state of the body at rest and where we want to return to after states of activation. Shutdown/collapse is the state of immobilization in response to fear. A lot of spoonies are chronically in a state of shutdown/collapse, fight/flight, or they bounce back and forth between the two states. This can take an enormous toll on our physiology, causing digestive

---

2 Stanley Rosenberg, Accessing the Healing Power of the Vagus Nerve: Self-Help Exercises for Anxiety, Depression, Trauma, and Autism (Berkeley, CA: North Atlantic Books, 2016).

issues, depressive episodes, chronic anxiety, insomnia, dysautonomia, and many other chronic health challenges.

Stephen Porges coined the term "neuroception" to describe how the neural circuits distinguish whether a situation is dangerous, threatening, or safe. Our bodies are performing neuroception constantly, scanning externally and internally through the senses to evaluate our environment and the state of our bodies. Sometimes we experience faulty neuroception, when the circuits from perception to behavior do not function the way they are supposed to. When experiencing faulty neuroception we react to a dangerous situation as if it is safe, or a safe situation as if it is dangerous. Faulty neuroception can have many causes, including being in physical pain, having an illness, being in a state of shock, being hungry, chemical interference from prescription drugs, remembering a traumatic event, or even falling in love. Faulty neuroception can be fleeting or last for months, years, or the rest of our lives, as is common for individuals who have experienced acute traumatic events or complex trauma. I want to highlight that faulty neuroception can cause illness or be caused by illness itself. My suspicion is that a lot of us in the spoonie community are living with some degree of faulty neuroception.

Thankfully nervous system dysregulation (chronic activation of dorsal vagal or sympathetic chain) is not necessarily permanent, and we are learning more about how to work with the ANS to achieve more regulated states. For example, we can move out of a shutdown/collapse or fight/flight state by activating the branch of the vagus nerve that regulates social engagement—and there are some simple ways to do that once you're regularly tracking your nervous system. The more you can track and work *with* your nervous system, rather than against it, the more ease and success you can experience in our healing journey. This could look like pursuing more activities and exercises that activate social engagement, working with practitioners who are polyvagal-literate, and/or considering your nervous system in your healing decisions. For example, guided breathwork has grown in popularity, but some of the practices can be very intense and might not be the best next step for *your* body at this time. If you're in the practice of tracking your nervous system, it will be easier to know if that medicine is a good fit for you at any given time.

You can start by simply observing what is happening in your body, without judgment. Do you feel tense? Relaxed? Heavy? Exhausted? Jittery? What do you notice about your heart rate? Digestion? Wherever you are is ok and know that many other humans around the world are having a similar experience! I recommend cultivating a habit of checking in with your nervous system like this a few times throughout the day. If you feel dysregulated, there are many practices that you can use on the fly and over time to regulate your nervous system and activate the state of social engagement. Some practices are designed to help you move out of shutdown/collapse, while others are meant to help you move out of fight/flight. The goal is always to get back to or spend more time in the social engagement state. I'll share some tools for self-regulation and co-regulation shortly. The tools and practices I share may not work for you, and that doesn't mean there is anything wrong with you or your body. There are many different approaches out there, and it's possible that you need different tools or additional support to experience more regulation. After the vaccine injury I experienced, I found that my previous go-to self-regulation tools didn't work as well as they had before. Co-regulation and bodywork were much more effective for me.

If you are in a state of fight/flight, something as simple as taking a deep breath with a long, slow exhale can instantly cultivate a sense of calm for your body and brain. As Ashley Neese explains in her book, *How to Breathe: 25 Simple Practices for Calm, Joy, and Resilience,*[3]

---

3 Ashley Neese, How to Breathe: 25 Simple Practices for Calm, Joy, and Resilience (California: Ten Speed Press, 2019).

During inhalation, the heart gets stimulated to beat a little faster. During the following exhale, the heart gets a message to slow down. The overall effect is very little change in the heart rate from minute to minute. However, when you make one part of the breath cycle, either the inhale or the exhale, longer than the other, and you do this for several minutes, the accumulated effect is that you will either slow your heart rate down or speed it up, depending on where you begin. When you extend your exhale by one to two counts longer than your inhale and you practice this for a couple of minutes, your heart rate will slow down. This sends a feedback message to the brain saying that everything is more peaceful and calm than it was a few minutes ago. This lets the brain support this shift further by turning on the rest-and-digest mode of the nervous system, which goes back from the brain to the body. The amazing thing is that the lungs and the heart can send feedback to the brain and essentially convince the brain that things are calm and peaceful, even when there are still stressful circumstances or anxiety-provoking thoughts circulating the mind.

You can also manipulate the breath to help you move out of a state of shutdown/collapse by lengthening the inhale, which will speed up your heart rate. You might try this if you're feeling extra fatigued, frozen, or heavy. Somatic coach Jacey Eve taught me a lovely practice that involves feeling into both forces that operate on the Earth—gravity and its opposite ground reaction force—while you breathe.[4] If you're in a jumpy dysregulated state, noticing gravity can be really grounding. If you are feeling like a ton of bricks, like gravity has got you down, you can put your attention on gravity's opposite, ground reaction force. I experience this as a sense of buoyancy in the inhale after the exhale. I visualize the exhale coming down to the ground and the inhale

---

4 This practice was informed by Jacey's training in Aston-Patterning® with Judith Aston.

bouncing me back up, like a ball bouncing up into the air. When I'm feeling really heavy and tired, even a minute of the bouncy inhale practice can completely change my experience. For more breathwork practices that support regulation, see Affirmations, Breathwork, and Yoga Practices in the Train Your Brain chapter of Section 3.

To move out of fight/flight, you can also try wrapping yourself up in a blanket like a burrito. This will help your brain stop running around in frantic circles. I ran a virtual workshop early in the COVID-19 pandemic in which I had everyone wrap themselves in a blanket in the beginning and stay wrapped for the rest of the workshop. It really changed the energy of our virtual space. I regularly use the practice myself when I'm having a hard day. I'll lie on the couch in the fetal position, completely wrapped up in a blanket and stare at the wall or close my eyes and focus on my breath if I have the wherewithal to do so. It's even better if you can get someone to tuck the blanket in tightly around you or swaddle you the way you would an infant. A blanket is also a nice addition to a restorative yoga practice. For example, you can wrap yourself in a blanket during a supported half frog pose (lying face down with a pillow under your torso, with one of your legs extended out to the side, bending the knee at about a 90 degree angle), or in savasana, also called corpse pose or final resting pose (lying on your back, eyes closed, with your legs hip width apart and palms facing up).

For cultivating regulation more generally, Resmaa Menakem recommends humming, rocking, rubbing the belly, om-ing, chanting, and a practice called "20's," which involves slowly rotating ankles, wrists and other joints in both directions 20 times each, with a ten second pause between each set of rotations.[5] I sometimes enjoy meditating for five to ten minutes and then lying on the floor and making noises. I try to allow whatever sound wants to emerge to emerge. Sometimes it's a scream or a deep moan. My neighbors probably think I'm bananas,

---

5 Menakem, My Grandmother's Hands: Racialized Trauma and the Pathway to Mending Our Hearts and Bodies.

ROR

but it really works for me, sometimes even eliciting a postcoital feeling in my body and mood.

Working with the nervous system is also something we can share with others and play with in a group context. In *My Grandmother's Hands*, Menakem shares practices you can do with other people to calm and synchronize the collective nervous system of a group. He suggests humming together, singing together, or inviting each person to rub their own belly in a circular motion. I've started introducing this as a practice folks can do together at the beginning of meetings or workshops to harmonize all the bodies in a room (it even works in virtual "rooms.") Consensual touch, playing together (including games), making music together, and storytelling are also nice tools for co-regulating the nervous systems in a group, even with just two or three people. Snuggling, massaging, singing, or dancing with a friend, lover, or family member can also serve as co-regulation.

These are some practices to get you started. There's a lot more out there and I recommend exploring and experimenting. I do not mean to suggest that you can pull yourself out of a dysregulated state overnight with a few deep breaths. It takes regular practice over time. Integrating nervous system awareness into your life won't solve all your problems, but it may give you some leverage in a healing context that you otherwise don't have a lot of control over. If, because of trauma or external circumstances, you experience chronic stress, regulation may feel harder to access with the suggested practices. That is not your fault. Because we do not have good systems in this country for providing care to chronically ill people, many folks in our community experience chronic stress just trying to meet their basic needs. If this is the case for you, I recommend trying to expand your support network as much as you can (even if only online) and look for opportunities to practice co-regulation in ways that feel safe to you. This might look like joining a mutual aid group or support group, asking someone to hang out with you (even remotely) as you do other things, and/or connecting with fellow sick and disabled individuals in online forums. I talk more about how to build community in Section 3.

EXERCISE:

Pick a day to do some nervous system awareness practice. Set an alarm or reminder to check in with your nervous system three times throughout the day and in your healing journal, record what you notice about your energy, without judgment. Do you feel anxious, calm, jumpy, relaxed, heavy? If you notice that you might be in a dysregulated state, try one of the simple exercises mentioned in this chapter, notice what happens, and record what you experience in your healing journal.

Bonus: Ask a friend or family member to try a co-regulation exercise with you. If you both laugh about how silly it feels, this can support regulation!

Step 2: Make Your Life Easier

Another great healing practice is to mitigate sources of stress wherever and whenever possible and look for opportunities to bring more ease to your day-to-day experience. There are a lot of stressors that we cannot easily control alone, like pollution in our immediate environment, income inequality, pandemics, or election results. Here we are going to look at ways to de-stress that *are* within our control. I'll offer both ways to remove stressors and add ease to your healing journey. These will be appropriate for many but not all bodies and minds. Support or modifications may be necessary.

Since even allopathic doctors tell us to reduce stress, maybe you've already done a lot in this department. If so, good job. You get a gold star! But let's be real, just being sick and/or in pain all the time is stressful in and of itself. Throw in work, kids, and other responsibilities, the oppressive forces of this country's power structures, and you might be like, "What IS this life?!" Regardless of what you've done so far to reduce stress in your life, there may be room to make things a little easier for yourself.

Stress reduction could be as extreme as leaving your current life behind and moving to the beach, or as simple as creating a new resting place for your keys so that you never lose them. But before you decide what actions to take, I invite you to really take an inventory of things in your life that create stress. Sometimes we aren't fully cognizant of our stress triggers so it can be helpful to bring a friend, partner, or family member into the process and ask them, "What do you notice stresses me out a lot?"

The following exercise can help you start building awareness around what adds stress to your life:

1. Write down the activities and situations in your life that feel most stressful.
2. Star the ones you have control over.
3. Look at the things you have control over and assess which ones you're *willing* to change right now. Circle those. (For example, you might have the ability to leave your job but you might not be willing to leave right now and that's okay.)
4. Look at the circled items and have a little brainstorm. Again, this is a great thing to do with another person. Are there any things on your list that you can reduce, cut out of your life, or delegate to someone else? And/or is there some support you're willing to ask for to make any of these just a little bit easier on yourself?

Examples:

Stress Trigger 1: Grocery shopping! It's hard on my body and because of my work schedule, I can only go during hours when it's really crowded. Crowds make me anxious.

Possible Solutions:
- Ask friends (Bob, Tina?) to go with me
- Get groceries delivered
- Ask neighbors Tim and Jamal to pick up groceries for me when they buy theirs
- Some combination of the above to save money and keep it easier for T&J since they're new parents

Stress Trigger 2: Getting dressed in the morning when brain fog is the worst.

Possible Solution: Take five minutes to lay out clothes the night before.

Once you identify and remove or mitigate some stress triggers, continue to be on the lookout for opportunities to make life a little easier for yourself. Once you begin to take steps to reduce stress and tune your antenna to be on the lookout for stress triggers, you'll start to see more and more opportunities to make life a little easier for yourself. Try on what it would feel like to become the Marie Kondo[6] of de-stressing and notice what it does for your wellbeing.

Because healing from complex health challenges can require a lot of significant lifestyle changes, such as eating special foods, taking lots of medicine, and moving through the world in different ways, it's helpful to approach the lifestyle side of healing with a healthy dose of experimentation and playfulness. If you try something and it's a total failure, then you can be grateful for the lesson and you can try something else. No need to beat yourself up. It's a great opportunity to practice self-love and compassion. If you are hard on yourself or experience the nothing-is-ever-going-to-work internal conversation, know that you're not alone, and keep breathing. Every spoonie in the world has struggled with at least some of the changes they've had to make.

When experimenting, I've found it useful to align to the following themes:
- Ease
- Energy conservation
- Nourishment

---

6 Marie Kondo is founder of the KonMari Method, which recommends tidying up by category and only keeping things in your life that spark joy. She is author of the bestselling book The Life-Changing Magic of Tidying Up, and star of the Netflix show "Tidying Up With Marie Kondo."

When you're making decisions day-to-day about what to eat, how to get somewhere, or how to get chores done, for example, you can ask yourself:

- **Ease: How can I make this easier on myself?**
  This is a great one to ask when you wake up feeling like you're going to have a hard or stressful day. Can you move appointments around so you don't feel rushed? Or change your transportation plans so they're a little easier? Can something be rescheduled?

- **Energy conservation: What is the least energy-intensive way to do this?**
  Can you break something down in small steps instead of going at it all at once and exhausting yourself? Can you get support with part of a task so your portion is more manageable?

- **Nourishment: What will be the most nourishing choice for me right now?**
  One day the answer might be drinking celery juice and going on a walk. Another day it might be eating ice cream and watching Netflix.

Let these questions be your compass. Regularly asking them of yourself is an opportunity to flex the muscles of listening to your body and your intuition. The more you ask them, the more you will develop routines and systems that work for you specifically. Over time, you may find that life will get progressively easier, less stressful, and more enjoyable.

Step 3: Maintain a Mindfulness Practice

If you don't already have a daily grounding and connection practice, I want to encourage you to test the waters and give you a few suggestions to play with. I'll say more about just how mindfulness supports healing in the Train Your Brain chapter in Section 3.

Alex Amorosi, one of my yoga and meditation teachers, says that in these times it's no longer okay *not* to have a regular practice of washing out your brain. It's as important to your physical vitality as brushing your teeth. And us spoonies in particular, because we have more stress and less energy to begin with, can benefit tremendously from having a practice that slows us down. At the most basic level, this practice is you-time that creates space for you to connect with your body, and perhaps forces greater than yourself. My practice often involves connecting with my breath and so I personally think about it as time to remember and *feel* that I am alive, and that being alive is a gift.

Your practice does not have to be a big deal, and it doesn't have to take a lot of time. It could look like meditation, coloring, yoga, mindful walking, or taking 10 minutes to stare out the window and watch birds do their thing. If you do not already have some kind of practice, meditating for even 10 minutes a day can be a great place to start. Traditionally meditation is practiced sitting but you can practice in any position that feels comfortable, or as comfortable as possible, for your body. For example, you can meditate lying in your bed, as long as you can stay awake for it. That's how I started my meditation practice. I did 10 minutes in the morning, in bed, right after I woke up. Gradually, as my physical capacity grew, I moved into a seated practice and added more time. I still often practice in a reclined or semi-reclined position, lying back over a yoga bolster.

If you have the ability to go to a meditation center and learn meditation from experts, that might be sweet for you, but you can get started with guided meditations on YouTube, or the Headspace and Insight Timer apps. I especially like Insight Timer because it has thousands of guided meditations and courses for all levels and on many themes, such as being with grief, getting to sleep, and healing physical pain. It also has a timer for when you want to practice meditation unguided. The app allows you to track your progress and connect with friends so if you're worried that you won't stick to your practice, you can recruit a buddy and keep tabs on each other through the app. Insight Timer also gives you stats on how much and how often you're meditating. You acquire stars for achieving different milestones, like meditating every day for 30 days. It's almost as good as getting a sticker! As of this writing, Insight Timer is free to use, though you have to pay for the courses it offers.

If you have anxiety, or you really struggle with being still, meditation might *not* be the best place to start. Meditation requires us to be mindful of our thoughts and shift our attention to the present moment, often using the breath as an anchor. If you're stuck in looping negative thoughts, it could feel more accessible to do something a little more active, or outside your brain, like bird watching, saying a mantra, breathing exercises, coloring, or moving your body. That said, some folks with anxiety love meditation, so see what works for you. I really love observing nature as a mindfulness practice. Sometimes it's looking at a flower, watching trees sway in the breeze, listening to birds, or noticing what the ants at my feet are up to. The practice is simple and you can do it almost anywhere. There's usually something to see, even in the cracks of the sidewalk or the bushes at the edge of a parking lot.

Whatever you choose to experiment with, let it be something that you can do daily. You might start by simply taking a few deep breaths and staring at the wall for three minutes a day. Take note of any shifts in your energy and record it in your healing journal. That will allow you to revisit positive results later, which you can use as motivation to keep going. Your nervous system will thank you, and I guarantee you'll start to feel a little bit lighter. If you miss a day, just start again. There's no way to be perfect at meditating so all you perfectionists are just going to have to deal with being imperfect on this front. Love you! Sorry not sorry! But seriously, maybe letting go of doing it "right" alone will be a great practice for you. Enjoy!

Step 4: Write a Vision Statement for Your Healing Journey

So far, we've looked at tracking and calming your nervous system, centering and grounding yourself with mindfulness practices, and strategies for making your day-to-day life a little easier. The next foundational step is to establish a vision, or guide star, to inform and support your healing journey. In astronomy, a guide star is used as a reference to maintain the alignment and tracking of a telescope while the earth rotates.[1] Having a vision is invaluable when you're on the healing path. Typically healing journeys are nonlinear and at least a little, if not very, tumultuous. This can make healing unpleasant, and sometimes you just won't feel like doing what's required of you. But having clarity on what all your hard work is for, and having something to come back to when the going gets tough, can drastically shift the energy of healing in a more enjoyable, more easeful direction.

Vision writing is my favorite tool for bringing more clarity, ease, alignment, and focus to the healing journey. More specifically, I recommend writing a vision statement that spells out what you'd really love your life to look like, including any healing objectives you hope to achieve. A vision statement invites you to imagine a more desirable lived experience, slightly or perhaps drastically outside the realm of what you think is possible. It describes the dreamiest dream—the best-case scenario. Allowing yourself to dream big is often challenging, but coaxing yourself into envisioning what you might love and writing it down creates the opportunity for you to go out into the world and see if what you want *is* actually attainable. Every client I've worked with

---

1 "Guide Star," Wikipedia, June 9, 2022, https://en.wikipedia.org/wiki/Guide_star.

has experienced doubt in the visioning process and has been blown away by what they were able to achieve in their life and in their healing after they wrote down their wildest dreams. It's powerful.

I'm going to share *how* to write an effective vision statement, then give you a few more reasons why I think it's a great exercise to support your healing.

My favorite way to write a vision is in the first person, in the present tense, and with very specific, vivid details.[2]
It might sound like:

> I am so pleased that I started my own social impact graphic design business. I'm inspired by my clients and I love that my creativity directly supports their work towards our collective liberation. My flexible schedule and annual income of $105,000 allow me to take care of myself and my family with ease. I'm able to see the doctors I want, send my kids to an afterschool program they love, and volunteer with a local mutual aid organization. My favorite part of being a business owner is getting to do so much work from home, in my pajamas, with Tex the beagle at my feet. I still feel the ups and downs of illness but I have more space to love on my body and I feel really supported by friends and neighbors. I move through the world with more joy, in greater connection with others.

When you write a vision statement this way, you are already there, living from the vision.

Let's assume the person who wrote this vision is currently working a so-so part-time job and feels pretty sick and stressed most of the

---

2 I learned this approach from my friend and coach Jeremy Blanchard, who adapted it from Mary Morrissey (https://www.marymorrissey.com/). Vision boards are cool too. I'm more of a writer and I prefer the specificity and vivid details that come with a written vision. If you would rather make a vision board, with images that represent what you want out of this healing thing, knock yourself out. You can even do both! Many of my clients do.

time. Even though this vision as reality could feel nearly impossible at the moment, there are small steps the writer of this vision can take immediately to start living from that vision, like speaking to a self-employed graphic designer to learn more about freelancing in the industry.

I also recommend giving your vision a name, e.g. "Lazlo's Kickass Life," and putting a date on it, e.g. September 1, 2027. Sometimes it can be helpful to write a short-term and a long-term vision. That could look like a one-year and a five-year vision, or a two-year and a ten-year vision, for example. Whatever feels most helpful for you.

People often ask me how long their vision statement should be. It doesn't really matter, but somewhere between three paragraphs and two pages is probably good. The more detail, the better. I recommend including specifics about what you'd love in multiple aspects of your life, including your health, relationships, work, home, family, social contributions, activities, and whatever feels relevant and important to you. You can also write multiple visions: a vision for your healing, a vision for your dream house, a vision for your ideal partner…you get the idea.

To get started, spend some time tuning in with yourself. For me, this always looks like lying on the floor, on a rock, or in a hammock with my eyes closed. Then allow yourself to consider the question, "If anything was possible, and there was no possibility of failure, what would I really love out of my healing journey?"

You can also ask yourself any of these questions that resonate:
- What would an ideal day in my life look like?
- Who is on my team?
- Where do I want my healing to take me?
- What kinds of support do I have?
- What would achieving my healing goals allow me to do, for myself and my community?

Write about what you see and experience in response to these questions. See if you can write everything that comes up, without judgment.

Regarding the last question, an important outcome of the visioning process is getting some clarity on *why* you're healing. In my case, my healing journey is in service of more personal and collective freedom. I am healing so that I can feel freer, and therefore experience more joy. And this will help me support others to feel the same. I want to deprogram myself of internalized oppression and resist external forces of oppression so I can get off the crushing hamster wheel of capitalism, for example. Two of my more specific personal motives for healing are 1) to lightly hold the possibility that I might be able to resume some of the outdoor activities I love, with people I love, like running, biking, swimming, kayaking, and maybe even backpacking, and 2) having the capacity to support more people in their healing, which is work that I love.

Everyone's vision is different. There's really no way it *should* look or sound, so you can do what works for you. You'll know you've got a solid vision statement when reading it gets you pumped up, even if part of you is saying, "No way, you silly idealist." That means you're onto something. The rest of this book is going to support you in making your vision real, so if worries or doubtful internal conversations arise when you're writing. Just do the best you can. If it starts out as a list of bullet points, right on. Also, what you write doesn't ever have to be a final draft. A vision statement should be a living document that changes over time as you get clearer about what you want, and clearer about what's actually possible. If you get stuck in the process, ask people in your life for some support. Let them remind you what you get excited about and what you're capable of.

Once you have a written vision statement, the next step is to let it really sink into your being. Read it aloud to yourself. Notice what you feel in your body as you read it and visualize yourself having what you describe in your vision. You might even move or dance with the feeling of it if that's accessible to you. I recommend hanging up your vision statement where you can see it, placing it on an altar, putting it under your pillow, or whatever supports you to spend time with it daily for at least a month. During that month, I invite you to start taking some small action steps to begin to make the vision real. I recommended choosing a small first step that feels both energizing and attainable, and something that you can actually do in physical reality, like making a phone call, conducting some research to make a list of options, or asking a friend to help you with a task.

Once you take your first step, celebrate! This is really important. Do not skimp on the celebration. Celebrating with others is awesome, but if that's not available, or you're not ready to do that, at least look at yourself in the mirror and say, "Yay! I did a thing!" Then, take your next small step. Important note: acting on your vision doesn't have to be a rushed, overwhelming thing. You get to determine the pace of your actions.

We know that this write–act–celebrate approach will exponentially increase the likelihood of you creating the life you'd love, because we have the science to prove it! Dr. Gail Matthews of Dominican University in California found that when you write down your goals regularly you are 42% more likely to score them. And if you share them with someone else, the favorable odds increase even more.[3]

If science isn't enough to convince you, here are a couple more reasons why everyone on a healing journey should write a vision statement:

1. Having a vision helps you save energy(!!!). This is for two reasons:

   a. **Having a vision can support you to pursue your healing in the way that is most authentic to you.** It will support you to act in alignment with your

---

3 Mary Morrissey, "The Power of Writing down Your Goals and Dreams," HuffPost, December 7, 2017, https://www.huffpost.com/entry/the-power-of-writing-down_b_12002348.

values and what's important to you. I probably don't have to tell you that everyone and their mom has opinions about what you should do to heal, and it's easy to get overwhelmed with all the options and approaches. Your vision will spell out how you want your healing to look, and you can revisit that when you're feeling unsure. Not sure where to invest your energy? Instead of spinning out or making never-ending pros and cons lists, you can ask yourself, what would someone with this vision do? What actions would they take? Whenever you're stuck on a decision or not sure what to do, you can revisit your vision with these questions in mind. Typically, the answers come more easily than they would when working without a vision statement.

b. **A vision statement can help you find support.** When you read your vision statement, you will see more clearly where you need the support of others to fulfill your vision, and you will be better prepared to ask for what you need. It will be easier for you to communicate about what you're wanting and needing, and it will be easier for folks to see how important your vision is to you. People in your life will see the way your vision lights you up, which in turn will light them up, and they will be extra pumped to support you. The response of friends and loved ones may sound like, "Hell yeah, I want to help you get a new mobility device so you can live the dream of taking your daughter to Legoland," or whatever it is you'd love to do: start a business, travel with your sweetie, write a book, start a movement, grow your houseplant collection... the possibilities are endless.

I'll say more about how to enroll support in Section 3, Build a Support Dream Team.

2. The process of visioning is a good opportunity to practice dreaming. Dreaming is a crucial part of the other benefits I described above. Knowing what the dream is allows you to be more strategic and *aligned* in your actions. The increased clarity and focus allow you to save energy and experience more success with the actions that you take. This is true both personally and collectively. Groups working together for social change also need to spend time dreaming about the future they want so that they know where they are going. Practicing dreaming in your own life will support you in dreaming with others.

I also want to acknowledge that depending on how ill, addicted, or chewed up by the systems you are, dreaming may feel inaccessible. When I lead the workshops for folks with health challenges specifically, at least one participant will initially balk at the exercise and say they don't have the capacity to dream past where they're currently at because of brain fog, grief, or depression. If that comes up for you, ask yourself, "Even if I don't know what it looks like or what it feels like, am I willing to envision a different reality for myself?" If the answer is "yes," take a few deep breaths, close your eyes and see what comes up. Maybe that's your daily homework for the next nine months. Trust that the vision will come. Even if you can't dream today, it doesn't mean you're not capable of dreaming anymore. It might just mean that some things need to shift before you can access it again. I believe in you.

If you ask, "am I willing to envision a different reality for myself?" and the answer is "no," you're not willing, come back to this exercise another time. Or, sometimes, it's helpful to start with a list of all the things you don't want, like "I don't want to be in pain when I walk to the mailbox." Once you write out the list of what you don't want, make a list of statements that illustrate the desired alternatives. For example, "I love that I can walk to the mailbox without pain." These statements will give you the bones of a vision statement in no time!

I recommend revisiting your vision statement every three to six months to see if it needs any adjustments or upgrades. When you read it after some time has passed, notice what in your vision has already happened even without you putting a lot of energy into it. Log this in your healing journal. Again and again, I've seen folks make their visions real, even in the face of huge obstacles. Whether it's the result of focusing your attention, sharing your dreams with others, or plain ole magic, it's a very effective way to shift your experience over time and create the life you would really love. If you want additional support to get the visioning process done, please contact me through my website, noellejanka.com. I have many offerings on this topic, including live workshops, recordings, and one-on-one visioning coaching.

Step 5: Cultivate a Mindset of Gratitude and Abundance

It can be challenging to craft and pursue a vision when you are feeling unwell. The experience of living with chronic pain and illness breeds a mindset of scarcity, which increases suffering and makes it harder to heal. Here we'll look at how you can overcome your brain's natural propensity for scarcity by practicing gratitude and generosity, which will help you cultivate more hopefulness and generally bring more satisfaction to your life and healing.

Our brains are naturally wired to see the glass half empty, and feeling poopy all the time really amplifies that. Without even realizing it, we become especially present to what we don't have. It starts with the health or mental health we don't have and then it bleeds into other areas until we have a long list of real or perceived lack. Unfortunately, chronic illness often does precipitate loss. Sick and disabled folks will lose friends, family, jobs, and sometimes their sense of self. And the more you lose, the harder it can feel to be present to what you still have.

This experience of getting caught up in what we lack is very normal. It's part of the negativity bias—our brain's propensity to attend to, learn from, and use negative information far more than positive information. It's a biological adaptation designed to keep us safe, so we can have compassion for ourselves. But we want to avoid this inclination from going into overdrive mode. When you're already feeling bad all the time, and maybe freaked out about money, energy, or whatever else is in short supply, it can feel like the negativity bias is taking over your life. And as you may have experienced, this scarcity spiral can cause tremendous stress of its own.

Thankfully, we have the capacity to shift our attention and we can practice being more interested in what we have rather than what is missing. I'll share more about this in Section 3: Train Your Brain but want to offer some initial thoughts here. You can train your brain to be on the lookout for all the things you do have and the things that are good, instead of getting sucked into the juicy story about what you don't have. Sometimes this is called cultivating an abundance mindset. One of the easiest ways to do this is to intentionally and regularly name what you are grateful for. If expressing gratitude isn't already part of your spiritual or self-care practice, or you don't have one of those, I invite you to try it out. This might look like saying a prayer in which you express gratitude, or writing down three things you're grateful for each night before you go to bed. One of my colleagues writes down ten things she's grateful for every morning. My ex-partner and I would tell or text each other at least three things we were grateful for every night. We called it "Tudes." Because I had to share what I was grateful for each night, I was (and still am) more regularly on the lookout for what I'm grateful for. After a few years of having a gratitude practice, I have more days where I'm overcome with how much I have and how grateful I am. I tell more people how grateful I am for their presence in my life, and I experience more joy in small things. After a few months of doing "Tudes," I also noticed that both my partner and I did a lot less bitching and kvetching and spent more time talking about other things. When you regularly and consistently choose to be grateful, you begin to experience life as abundant. You see more of life's gifts instead of just life's challenges.

Just in case you need a little more persuading, science affirms that gratitude practices and cultivating an abundance mindset improve physical well-being.[4]

---

4 Misty Pratt, "The Science of Gratitude," Mindful, November 10, 2022, https://www.mindful.org/the-science-of-gratitude/.

The broad-ranging health benefits of gratitude can include better sleep, lessened anxiety and depression, and more emotional resilience. So, the more grateful you are, the more hopeful you are, and the less likely you are to experience those mental health challenges. And people who report higher levels of hope tend to have a higher pain tolerance, greater perceived health, and an easier time adjusting to health challenges.

That's what some science and I have to say about gratitude. Now it's time for you to give it a try. If writing what you're grateful for in a journal doesn't sound like your thing, ask someone in your life to be your gratitude buddy, and see what it's like to express gratitude with each other once a day for 21 days in a row. You can do it in-person, on the phone, or via text. Then sit back and enjoy as you begin to see your life as more abundant, lighter, and brighter.

If you want to take it a step further, start recording or reporting what you're grateful for about your body specifically. I also invite you to take stock of whatever upsides you've experienced in your journey so far, no matter how small, and notice what you feel in your body when you read your list. Expressing gratitude for the body, though often challenging for spoonies, can be a very generative and reparative practice.

Step 6: Pursue Joy & Pleasure

In addition to gratitude, joy and pleasure are essential ingredients in healing, and for a lot of spoonies we need to actively reintroduce them into our lives. Here we'll begin to look at why (re)connecting with our joy is important and how you might do it. We'll dive deeper into this subject in the Cultivate Self Love, Section 3.

When we get sick or injured, it's common to have to put your hobbies and passion projects on the back burner. It might be that you're physically not able to do what you love, or feel like you don't have the energy for it. When we have less energy, we naturally direct it towards survival. We spend it working (if we can), feeding ourselves, and doing other things that NEED to be done. We can feel like our lives are really nothing more than self-care routines and whatever else we need to do to survive. One of my clients captured this perfectly once when she despaired, "I feel like my life is just working and coffee enemas." If that sounds familiar, it's a good indication that it's time to up the joy factor in your life. Before you fight me and say there's no time for joy, hear me out.

Sprinkling a little more joy in your life doesn't have to be a big undertaking. That doesn't mean your mind won't give you a lot of evidence that it will be a lot of work though. The internal dialogue usually sounds something like, "I can't do what I used to do, the way I used to do it, so I can't do it at all," or, "Figuring out how to do things differently will take too much effort." It can sound silly when you say it out loud but sounds really true in your head. Another thing I see a lot is that people say they want to do something fun, like join a painting class, then they see some obstacles to that (time, money, energy), and then they quickly give up on the pursuit of joy altogether. Again, that reaction is natural, but things aren't often as black and white as our minds would have us believe. Our brain loves making things binary, but there are always options in between the extremes. If not a painting class, is there another way you could do some painting?

Overcoming the hurdles to cultivating joy requires some creativity and a willingness to start small. This could look like inviting some people who make you laugh to come hang with you at home, asking someone with more spoons to drive you somewhere, or researching different ways to do an activity you love. It may take a little experimentation to find something fun that matches up with the time and energy you have—but I believe in you. I'm guessing you're pretty crafty and resilient if you've made it this far!

If you're not sure where to start, begin by making a list of things that bring you joy, or used to bring you joy (sometimes we get really disconnected from it). Then, maybe with the support of a friend or loved one, list all the ways you might be able to realistically engage with each thing. From there, pick one possible pursuit from the list and ask yourself, "What is one small step I'm willing to take to make this happen?"

You might also look out for ways to add a little more joy and sweetness to your life in general. What would it be like to play a song you love while you brush your teeth for example? Personally, I love music and will frequently use music to coax myself into doing things I feel like I don't have the energy for, like cooking or doing dishes. This works because it ups the joy factor. This book, for example, was made possible by a lot of house music, jazz, and hip-hop instrumentals. I also practice choosing the more enjoyable option when making decisions about how to get somewhere, or how I want to complete a particular task. Like if I could walk, drive, bike, or take public transit somewhere, I'll try to pick the option that will bring my body and mind the most ease and pleasure, even if it takes longer.

If you start to feel resistance to adding joy into your life or asking others to help you with this joy pursuit, know that that's totally natural. This resistance is normal because we've all received a lot of conditioning about what joy is, how to experience it, and who is deserving of it. A lot of us can even trace our illness to repeatedly denying ourselves what brings us joy. Unraveling and overcoming the anti-joy conditioning and associated actions, as uncomfortable as it may be, is a critical ingredient to healing. You're just going to have to treat yourself and have a little fun along the way. So why not start now? I'll say more about joy in the Cultivate Self-Love in Section 3, but for now, I recommend doing the aforementioned reflection exercise, and suggest that you write "JOY" on a sticky note and put it somewhere where you can see it every day as a reminder, like on a mirror or as the background on your phone. Those are both effective ways to start to orient yourself towards things that are joyful.

SECTION 2

WHY HEAL?

Hopefully now you feel like you have a few more tools to support you on the healing path. Now, I'm going to explore the reasons why pursuing healing is so worthwhile for you and the collective. We will also explore the importance of understanding the context in which we are healing and the importance of seeing ourselves in the broader collective of sick individuals living on Turtle Island.[5]

Being willing to heal involves being willing to acknowledge and heal the generations of trauma and programming that have forged our personal and collective unwellness. Once you understand the truly systemic nature of disease, you can't help but see how we are all affected and need to lift each other up and change the status quo together. In this way personal healing is a tremendous contribution

---

5 Many Indigenous groups refer to North America as Turtle Island.

to you, your community, and our collective liberation from systemic oppression. I'll explain more about this in the pages to come, but for starters, let's look at you, and how resolving to heal can free up your energy and attention in big ways.

Committing to Your Own Healing

"Heal so you can hear what's being said without the filter of your wounds. Heal so you can see what is before you beyond the blinders of your wounds."
—Dr. Thema Bryant-Davis

We are not meant to be in pain all the time. If that has been your reality for years, though, it can be hard to remember what life was like without it. You might even feel like the back pain, foot pain, cough, stomachaches, chronic migraines, dysautonomia, all-consuming depression—whatever you experience—is just part of who you are. If you and your doctors aren't able to find a root cause, that can make it feel even more like your condition isn't changeable. Maybe you've struggled with the feeling that it's all in your head.

If you've had this experience, you know how devastating and frustrating it can be to feel like you have no solutions. It's not surprising that a lot of us give up on finding the cause and do our best to ignore or push through whatever pain we are experiencing. It can seem like our best option, or our only option. Acceptance is also an option, but it doesn't come naturally because societal norms tend to steer most of us toward the "suck-it-up" approach.

No judgment if you've been on the "suck-it-up" path. It really is the only option in some cases, but I want to take a moment to examine the consequences of ignoring our pain and illness and explore how and why it's worth pursuing a sense of acceptance of where your body is at, if possible. I want to distinguish here between accepting the state of your body vs. accepting the state of the context that created your illness. You do not have to forgive your abusers for example, in order to accept that your body is in pain. What I'm talking about here is telling the truth about your body being in pain.

When you ignore pain and other symptoms, you are ignoring a distress signal from your body. When ignoring the signal becomes your norm, it's like you're perpetually living on a sinking ship. Even if the ship is taking on just a little water for years without sinking, it's going to be pretty wet on board, and it certainly is not going to get to port anytime soon. As the captain of this ship, part of you is also at least a little worried about drowning or expending a lot of energy trying to override or ignore the fear of drowning. If the ship is taking on a lot of water, you may be capsizing before you know it.

Being in this chronically stressful position can make you a jerk—to other people and/or yourself. That sounds harsh but think about it: if you have been living on a sinking ship, with soggy socks, exhausted from ignoring them, for weeks, months, or even years, it is only natural that the chronic unpleasantness creeps into the rest of your life and impacts your work, your relationships, and your everyday interactions. It saps your capacity to be patient, present, compassionate, kind, and loving—to others and yourself.

If you are living with a chronic condition and *have* embraced it, chances are you see the suffering in others all the time: that snippy woman at the grocery store, that man who gets unreasonably pissed at the café when his latte has the wrong milk in it. Once you have observed and acknowledged your own suffering, you see suffering everywhere, and you're able to be compassionate with those experiencing it. In a way, this frees up a lot of energy because you know not to take other people's rudeness or poopy attitude personally. You can just say "Yep, they're in pain."

No matter how much pain we are feeling personally, physically or otherwise, we can choose to be compassionate healers: heroines on our own healing journeys. The first step is simply being willing—willing to acknowledge your symptoms and do your best to get to the root of them, even if you're not sure how.

That is easier said than done, because acquiring and living with chronic health conditions is upsetting.

Once you understand that a health condition isn't temporary, you might find yourself in one of the following states of being:

- Spinning: Blaming yourself or others or worrying it's all in your head.
- Perpetual seeking: Desperately trying to find the solution or someone to "fix" it.
- Resignation: "I'm going to be in pain forever."
- Acceptance: "I understand that this is my current reality and I'm willing to work with it."

Usually, we start with one of the first two states. Sometimes you might hop back and forth between these different states depending on the day, how you feel, and what happened at your last doctor's appointment. That's all normal. While everyone deserves love and respect no matter what state they're in, I recommend working towards acceptance because it brings a lot more ease to everyday life, and the people around you.

Acceptance is necessary in healing because it creates space for you to move forward. It involves surrendering to and telling the truth about what is. It's usually less about doing anything in particular and more about stopping or *not* doing things that don't serve you. It's also about learning your edges, shadows, limits, and triggers, owning them, and learning how to be vulnerable with them and communicate about them clearly. For example, this could look like learning to own and communicate about your food restrictions without feeling shame about asking for special accommodations.

Acceptance can allow you to:
- Ride the inevitable waves of uncertainty with more ease.
- Be more authentic and present with others because you're not as tortured by our own suffering.
- Save energy!
- Create space to see what you need to do to heal because you won't be so wrapped up in the suffering anymore.

When you aren't oriented towards acceptance, you:
- Cannot be fully present or available with the people you love.
- Spend a lot of energy avoiding discomfort, or potential discomfort—physical, emotional, and otherwise.
- Take your suffering out on others and look for people to hold your pain.

How can you foster acceptance of your circumstances? I've found that learning to see your health challenges in context creates more space for acceptance. The short version is that there is a chronic illness epidemic in the U.S. and many of us are doomed to be sick before we even emerge from the womb. Just in case you thought you were alone with your experience, you're very much not. We live in a modern world that puts up A LOT of barriers to being healthy. Worse still, our healthcare system isn't equipped to deal with our illness and largely exacerbates our collective unwellness.

The experience of being chronically sick or in pain and waking up to how sick our whole society is, is pretty painful in itself. This is why acceptance is usually preceded by a period, or multiple periods of rage, grief, confusion, sadness, and, for some folks, an intense desire to right the societal wrongs that have landed us where we are. Sometimes feeling all those feelings happens in pretty swift succession, but for some it takes years, particularly if we don't feel safe feeling our feelings. That was my experience for a long time, and I've seen it in a lot of other spoonies too. Feeling through these phases is an essential part of the healing process. The more you resist the feels, the longer it takes to heal. Conversely, if you allow yourself to grieve, rage, and cry (I'll talk more about how to do that in Section 3) that will help your body heal faster. I want to emphasize though that speed is not the goal. It's going to take as long as it's going to take. But that said, my hope is that with the support of this book and the support that you cultivate in your own life, you might experience more freedom and physical vitality with fewer trials and tribulations than I did, for your own benefit and for everyone around you. Approaching your healing with a collective orientation will bring you so much more ease and it may eventually free up some of your energy to work towards a world in which we experience better health outcome. I'll say more about this context in the next chapter, and more about other tools to foster acceptance later in Train Your Brain, Section 3.

Understanding Our Context

"We are not meant to thrive in isolation. We need each other to do well. If there are people down the street from you that are not well, you're not well. If there are people across the world that aren't well, you're not well. If our Earth is not well, we are not well."

—Andréa Renae Johnson

At the risk of being a downer, I want to spend a little time looking at just how we are set up to struggle with our health here in the United States. This is partly selfish, because I want to politicize you and enroll you in the healing revolution, but it's also meant to support you in understanding the lay of the land and how it may be shaping your experience with chronic illness. There are many reasons why chronic illness is the leading cause of death in the United States, and a majority of Americans are living with at least one chronic condition.[6]

Despite what doctors and wellness practitioners may have led you to believe, it's not all on you that you're sick. (It's also not all on you to heal, but we'll talk more about that later.) There's a lot working against you and your wellbeing. Once you can discern between what is truly yours to heal versus what is an external circumstance working against you—something that needs collective healing—you can begin to reclaim your power and agency.

To understand the roots of chronic illness in the United States, we first have to understand more about trauma.

---

6 "About Chronic Disease," Center for Managing Chronic Disease, accessed January 31, 2023, https://cmcd.sph. umich.edu/about/about-chronic-disease/.

Trauma can be personal and collective. It can result from anything the body perceives as a threat—abuse, a virus, racism, pollution, war, a car crash—and all trauma is a product of our environment. Trauma can include acute or repeated events like sexual assault, physical or emotional abuse, and/or ongoing trauma like oppression based on skin color, race, ethnicity, disability, intellectual ability, gender, gender expression, or sexual orientation, for example.

We have all endured some trauma, and it doesn't seem to matter how severe it is for it to really mess with your body's physiology. Trauma doesn't necessarily come from a traumatic event or experience itself, but from not having the opportunity to metabolize the experience and re-regulate the nervous system after a traumatic event. If someone experiences a traumatic event and immediately has the opportunity to co-regulate with another person for example, the experience may not manifest as trauma in their body and mind.

Sometimes a past acute physical or emotional trauma can be healed and disease or pain goes away. The cause of *chronic* disease is a physical or emotional trauma that cannot be resolved as simply. The root of chronic conditions is a combination of trauma, chronic stress, childhood patterning, and/or emotional repression. Trauma initiates dysregulation in the nervous system, which impacts all our bodily functions.

If you constantly experience oppression in your day-to-day life—for example consistently having to navigate racist treatment at work and in your community—this constant threat registers as chronic stress in the nervous system, which can lead to disease. Somatic therapist Tada Hozumi put it succinctly: "Trauma is how oppression manifests in the body."[7] In the U.S. many of us have largely lost the rituals and other opportunities for co-regulation that our ancestors had. This loss of many co-regulation opportunities and collective coping skills leaves us

---

7 Tada Hozumi, zoom conversation with the author, January 2019.

particularly vulnerable to being traumatized, perpetuating trauma, and experiencing chronic disease.

In the United States, oppressive systems are causing trauma en masse, inflaming the chronic illness crisis. In short, so many of us are sick because our culture and institutions are sick. And this cultural and institutional illness reproduces more generations of traumatized humans. Most trauma, and particularly intergenerational family and community trauma that manifests as abuse, addiction, violence, illness, and mental illness can all be linked to cultural and systematic oppression.

We all have trauma in our history, and we understand now, thanks to the scientific fields of social genomics and epigenetics, that social and environmental factors affect our gene expression and that our gene expression is shaped by the social and environmental factors that affected our ancestors. Uncle Joe didn't come out of the womb an abusive alcoholic. He was a product of his environment—the culture of his community, the policies in the country where he grew up, the trauma endured by his ancestors, and the way his parents or guardians inflicted their own trauma onto him.

Epigenetics helps us understand both individual and population level health outcomes. It is part of the constellation of factors that explain why African Americans experience the worst health outcomes of any ethnic group in the United States, though these phenomena are more often explained as an economic or healthcare access issue. African American babies born today carry the genetic residue of many generations of racialized trauma in their cells, which affects their physical and mental health. Other racial and ethnic groups carry the legacy of other traumas in their bodies, e.g. Jewish families and the trauma of genocide.

Arline Geronimus, a public health researcher and professor at the University of Michigan's Population Studies Center, coined the term "weathering" in 1992 to describe the effect of constant stress on the bodies of African American women and infants in particular. The stress they experience is a combination of systemic oppression in the form of racist policies and cultural oppression in the form of unconscious bias and microaggressions.

A particularly illustrative statistic is that Black women are 243% (nearly four times) more likely than white women to die during or shortly after childbirth. The infant mortality rate in the South Side of Chicago, one of the poorest and Blackest parts of the country, is more than twice the national average. In many American cities, adult life expectancy is 10-20 years shorter in communities of color as compared to other neighborhoods.

In Boston, where I lived for more than a decade, there is a 33-year gap in life expectancy between the historically Black neighborhood of Roxbury, where the lifespan is just under 59 years old, and the very affluent and whiter neighborhood of Back Bay, where the average person lives to age 92. This enormous gap is the legacy of redlining and historic underinvestment in Black, Indigenous, and people of color (BIPOC) communities.

The COVID-19 pandemic brought increased attention to the connection between persistent systemic racism and health outcomes. In a 2020 article in *Health Education & Behavior* that uses "the over-representation of Black death reported in Detroit, MI" as a case study, sociology professor Whitney N. Laster Pirtle wrote, "Racial capitalism is a fundamental cause of the racial and socioeconomic inequities within the novel coronavirus pandemic (COVID-19) in the United States."

Racial capitalism and white supremacy, in fact, are at the heart of so much of our collective suffering and specifically chronic illness in the United States. This goes centuries back to our country's enslavement of Black people, genocide of Indigenous peoples, and imperialism worldwide—all in the name of accumulating more and more capital.[8]

---

8 "Racial Capitalism," Wikipedia (Wikimedia Foundation, January 29, 2023), https://en.wikipedia.org/wiki/Racial_capitalism.

The relative wealth that the U.S. has accumulated today is directly linked to the genocide and theft of the sacred lands of Indigenous peoples, and the massive profits of a cotton industry made possible by enslaved Black Africans. This is at the foundation of our country's profit-driven, individualistic approach to wellness—which hurts us all, but particularly harms Black and Indigenous people. If you boil everything down, nearly or perhaps all social problems in the U.S. can be traced to some combination of the legacy of racial capitalism and persistent white supremacy.

Take our lack of universal healthcare as an example. As Heather McGhee outlines in her book *The Sum of Us: What Racism Costs Everyone and How We Can Prosper Together*, racism against Black people has blocked efforts to improve our healthcare system for everyone.

For example, in the 1950 Florida race for U.S. Senate, opponents of universal healthcare (wealthy businessmen and the physicians' lobby) exploited white fear and racial resentment to successfully unseat universal healthcare champion Senator Claude Pepper, printing photos of him with African Americans, including Black actor and communist activist Paul Robeson. More recently, politicians have also used racial resentment to foment opposition to the expansion of Medicare and the Affordable Care Act, because they were associated with President Barack Obama.[9]

Throughout U.S. history, groups of white people have feared that making public goods and services accessible to Black people would threaten their own access. This zero-sum narrative has allowed politicians and other power holders to limit access for all of us. The zero-sum fear among white voters is also another manifestation of trauma. Oppression against and domination of BIPOC individuals is borne out of the trauma that lives in white bodies. White-bodied trauma on this land is the legacy of the original colonizers and later immigrants

---

9 Heather McGhee, "Going Without," in The Sum of Us: What Racism Costs Everyone and How We Can Prosper Together (Random House Publishing Group, 2021), pp. 50-61.

of European descent who were themselves victims of oppression in Europe, and assimilated into domination patterns and racist social order after arriving in the U.S. Because we have not yet addressed the legacy of slavery, genocide, and land theft in this country, the symptoms of those original wounds (policies) persist in our systems, culture, institutions, and bodies today—perpetuating trauma and chronic illness generation after generation.

With this backdrop, it should come as no surprise that chronic disease is now the leading cause of death in the United States.[10] As of 2014, 60% of American adults had at least one chronic condition and 42% had multiple conditions.[11] That statistic includes hypertension, lipid disorders (like high cholesterol), mood disorders, anxiety disorders, diabetes, asthma and other upper respiratory disorders, heart disease, arthritis and other inflammatory joint disorders. It does *not* include conditions like late-stage Lyme, ME/CFS, Ehlers-Danlos Syndrome, Fibromyalgia, Long COVID of course, or many of the 60+ autoimmune diseases we have names for. As of 2011, at least 40% of America's children also had at least one diagnosed chronic condition.[12]

For my fellow visual learners, the chart illustrates some of the root causes of the broader American chronic disease epidemic. This is not an exhaustive list.

---

10 "About Chronic Diseases," Centers for Disease Control and Prevention (Centers for Disease Control and Prevention, July 21, 2022), https://www.cdc.gov/chronicdisease/about/index.htm.

11 Christine Buttorff, Teague Ruder, and Melissa Bauman, "Multiple Chronic Conditions in America," RAND Corporation, May 26, 2017, https://www.rand.org/pubs/tools/TL221.html.

12 "2018 National Survey of Children's Health," NSCH 2018: Number of current or lifelong health conditions, Nationwide, accessed March 2, 2023, https://nschdata.org/browse/survey/results?q=7344.

Social Problem	Contributing Factors	Root Causes
60% of Americans have at least one chronic illness ⟶	Lack of access to healthcare	Racial capitalism
	Inadequate healthcare* ⟶	White supremacy culture
Income Inequality	Physiological stress	Racism
Food Insecurity	Poverty/wage theft	Policies that reinforce^^
Homelessness	Grind culture	Policies that act as band aids to social problems rather than address root causes above
Educational disparities	Individual & collective trauma	
	Lack of access to healthy food	
	Lack of access to wellness programming	
	Lack of affordable housing	

With this I am trying to capture the experiences of people like myself who have had access to healthcare that caused harm and/or didn't help them find resolution or relief of their health challenges.

I share this because I think it's helpful to see that your illness is the natural byproduct of our modern social order. You are one of millions of canaries in the coal mine. In this context, it also becomes clear that you are not the only one responsible for your health challenges. Sure, you have some say in how you live your life and take care of yourself, and it's possible that you could maybe make different choices that allow you to experience different health outcomes—but my point is that our health isn't as entirely in our hands as many health care providers, wellness leaders, public health institutions, and family members would have us believe. There are so many cards stacked against our health.

The ongoing effect of these root causes of harm is evident in the growing prevalence of chronic illness and disparities across racial and ethnic identities. It's evident in the exclusion of Black and Indigenous women from the healing trades and resulting loss of healing wisdom. It's evident in our society's move away from community and toward a greater and greater worship of the individual, leading us to be more isolated in our attempts to heal. It's evident in the prevalence of harmful chemicals in our food and products, hurting us, our communities, and the land. In the rest of this chapter, I will provide some context about all the ways that our existing social order is set up to make us sick. The more we see how the social order causes harm, the more we can look to one another for support and turn toward something different—liberation for ourselves and all of our communities.

Underregulation of Toxins

"We have to challenge the idea that contamination is just the price of living in the modern world. Our bodies don't have systems to process plastics or flame retardants or pesticides. If contamination is the price of modern society, modern society has failed us."

—Russell Libby

The prevalence of chronic disease is also due to environmental and social degradation, which make our bodies less resilient and more susceptible to developing chronic conditions. At the heart of this is our dominant culture's disconnection from the Earth. This problem, fueled by racial capitalism's mandate of growth over all else, has driven a shortage of safe, healthy food with the introduction of genetically modified organisms (GMOs), pesticides, and antibiotics. Air and water pollution, toxins in our personal care products, and electro and magnetic field (EMF) radiation all pose grave threats to our health. We also work too much, sit too much, and stare at screens too much.

Not surprisingly, more recent policy decisions have reinforced this harmful legacy of profit over health. In the same way that U.S. legislation has historically legislated racism, such as with redlining, it has relatedly legislated poor health outcomes, making it very difficult for citizens to live safe and healthy lives. When it comes to toxins, for example, our regulatory systems are set up so that companies are free to poison us and then make money off of "treating" us without ever having to address the poison or help us heal completely. As a culture, we make a big deal of raising money to "cure" cancer without banning the chemicals or addressing the environmental contaminants that cause it. Sometimes our government makes companies clean up their messes, but it's a piecemeal response to a systemic problem. Monsanto, for example, which was acquired by the drugmaker and chemical company Bayer in June 2018, has been fined multiple times for spraying and storing illegal chemicals, but continues to produce lethal chemical products because they are legal and unregulated in the United States.[13]

For the sake of comparison, the European approach to environmental protection and chemical management employs something called the "precautionary principle" that considers even possible risk reason enough to ban certain chemicals. According to European Union (EU) law, the principle "...aims at ensuring a higher level of environmental protection through preventative decision-taking in the case of risk. However, in practice, the scope of this principle is far wider and also covers consumer policy, European Union (EU) legislation concerning food and human, animal and plant health."[14]

Plant health?! If only we were so lucky.

The U.S. government requires that *proof of harm* be demonstrated before taking regulatory action on chemicals and the bar for proof of harm is especially high. The Toxic Substances Control Act, which was designed to regulate the commercial use of hazardous chemicals, does not guarantee that chemicals are safe or ensure that chemicals are rigorously tested before going on the market, into our food packaging,

---

13 Jonathan Stempel, "Bayer's Monsanto Pleads Guilty to Illegal Hawaii Pesticide Spraying," Reuters (Thomson Reuters, November 22, 2019), https://www.reuters.com/article/us-bayer-monsanto-plea-hawaii/bayers-monsanto-pleads-guilty-to-illegal-hawaii-pesticide-spraying-idUSKBN1XW21N.

14 "The Precautionary Principle," EUR-Lex, accessed February 6, 2023, https://eur-lex.europa.eu/EN/legal-content/summary/the-precautionary-principle.html.

cosmetics, furniture, clothing, and other products we use. It also has not been updated since it was enacted in 1976.[15]

One striking example of how these regulatory differences play out is in the ingredients of cosmetics. Since our skin is our largest organ, beauty products are a prime vehicle for poisoning. The EU bans 1,328 chemicals from cosmetics that are known or suspected to cause cancer, genetic mutation, reproductive harm or birth defects. The FDA has only banned 11.[16] This is not surprising given the scope and power of the U.S. chemical industry. The U.S. is the largest national producer of chemical products globally and, with the exception of Germany, the largest exporter of chemicals. Including the pharmaceutical industry, the U.S. chemical output in 2016 was $767 billion, and we hold more than 45 percent of the global pharmaceutical market.[17]

It might make sense that a country that willfully poisons its own people would also spend more on healthcare. We do, but it isn't helping us get healthier. The United States spends more on healthcare than any other country, and twice as much as the other ten highest income-earning countries (United Kingdom, Canada, Germany, Australia, Japan, Sweden, France, the Netherlands, Switzerland, and Denmark). Yet, we have the lowest life-expectancy and the highest infant mortality rate of all eleven countries. The difference in spending costs is explained by higher hospital administration costs, higher salaries for doctors and nurses, and much higher pharmaceutical costs.[18] In 2016, spending per capita on pharmaceuticals was $1,443 in the U.S. as compared to a range of $466 to $939 in the other high-income countries. Perhaps not surprisingly, since we're literally bathing

15 "Getting Our (Toxic Substances) Act Together," Ensia, July 23, 2018, https://ensia.com/features/getting-our-toxic-substances-act-together/.

16 "Laws & Regulations," Safe Cosmetics, June 9, 2022, https://www.safecosmetics.org/resources/regulations/.

17 "Topic: Chemical Industry in the United States," Statista, accessed March 17, 2020, https://www.statista.com/topics/1526/chemical-industry-in-the-us/.

18 PhD Irene Papanicolas, "Health Care Spending in the United States and Other High-Income Countries," JAMA (JAMA Network, March 13, 2018), https://jamanetwork.com/journals/jama/article-abstract/2674671.

in carcinogenic toxins, five of the top 15 best-selling pharmaceuticals in the U.S. in 2016 were cancer drugs.[19]

There are brave souls and courageous organizations out there, like the Campaign for Safe Cosmetics, working hard to help people understand the connection between chemicals and our health, and proposing legislation that would keep us safer. The more average Americans understand this connection, the more we can build political will and redirect some of the "Race for the Cure" energy to pressure our elected leaders to stand up to special interests and protect their constituents from being poisoned. We also need to educate ourselves and each other about how best to protect our own health. And, even if we weren't being systematically poisoned for profit, we would still have the problem of national healthcare and social services systems that fail many by failing to address chronic illness and excluding the kinds of healers needed to ensure all are served.

A Society That Creates Chronic Illness En Masse, But Treats Wellness as the Norm

We can see that we live in a society that creates chronic illness as the norm without acknowledging its true origins. And because the epidemic of chronic disease isn't fully acknowledged, our system as a whole is poorly equipped to provide care for anyone who needs it for more than an acute episode. Our diagnostics and treatments are great for some conditions and virtually non-existent for others. They tend to favor diseases that affect cis men and that can be managed with pharmaceuticals. Many patients who experience long-term sickness are not recognized or supported in our system.

As Johanna Hedva brilliantly lays out in her *Mask Magazine* essay "Sick Woman Theory,"[20] we have a problematic societal expectation

19 Alex Philippidis, "The Top 15 Best-Selling Drugs of 2016," GEN, November 3, 2018, https://www.genengnews.com/lists/the-top-15-best-selling-drugs-of-2016/.

20 Johanna Hedva, "Sick Woman Theory," 2020, https://johannahedva.com/SickWomanTheory_Hedva_2020.pdf.

that wellness is the norm. Sickness is viewed as abnormal and also temporary. You're either sick or well, and if you're sick, it's assumed that you'll get better, reenter society, and work 40 hours a week like everyone else. When you can't, it's very difficult, maybe near impossible, for you to get the care you need.

When we are sick permanently, or for a significant period of time, the social service system doesn't know what to do with us. Our friends, family, and employers don't know either. Some sick folks are able to get disability benefits, which help with survival but can also leave them in a cycle of poverty and chronic stress that prevents them from being able to heal. And that's if you're lucky enough to actually be awarded disability benefits.

A lot of conditions aren't widely recognized as disabling, such as late-stage Lyme disease or Myalgic Encephalomyelitis (ME), and those patients are forced to appeal many times before they *maybe* get approved. At this writing, Long COVID patients are tragically being denied disability because it is not recognized as a disease while also being denied healthcare coverage because they have a pre-existing condition.[21]

A dear friend of mine who'd been bedridden with ME for more than a decade finally won Social Security Disability Insurance (SSDI) after two years of working nonstop with lawyers to appeal the initial denial. Less than a month later, she took her own life because she'd become unbearably ill and didn't see any path to healing given the uphill battle she still faced just to get the day-to-day care she needed.

She was 37 and, like me, had been sick since high school. After years of using her "tiny energy" as she called it, to coordinate friends and strangers to get even the most basic care she needed to stay alive, a heart condition left her unable to sleep or rest at all, and she opted

<hr>

21 Sarah O'Brien, "Long Covid Patients Can Face a Battle Trying to Claim Benefits through Their Workplace Disability Insurance," CNBC (CNBC, December 20, 2022), https://www.cnbc.com/2022/12/20/long-covid-patients-face-battle-claiming-disability-insurance-benefits.html.

out. She was an incredible human, and her decline was horrible and heart wrenching to witness.

Given how poorly understood ME is, it was too dangerous for her to be in a hospital or state-run care facility, and she wasn't well enough to travel to the doctors who could help her. She got some medical care over the phone, but there was only so much that could be done without testing, and only so much that was covered by insurance. Because she didn't have a terminal diagnosis, she also didn't qualify for assisted suicide in the states where it is legal.[22]

No one wanted to be implicated in her death, so she literally died alone. She fell through the cracks of our system and when her family couldn't be there for her, and her self-organized care network of friends and acquaintances couldn't provide all that was needed, there was nothing to catch her. And she is just one example of a whole section of our population that is left without options.

If you are always sick and always need care, you're largely left out and seen as a burden—on the economy, our healthcare system, communities, and families. The expectation that illness and care are temporary, and our failure to address the reality of chronic illness, literally kills people. It leaves the rest of us chronically stressed and, in many cases, full of shame and/or exhausted from needing to ask for support again and again, in many cases while supporting others, in a culture that doesn't provide or value care.

Patriarchy & Racism: The Roots of Our Systemic Lack of Care

We can attribute this dearth of care in part to patriarchy and racism. Care is seen as feminine and is therefore devalued and made invisible. You've probably noticed that the people who do the hardest and most

---

22 Final Exit is a Right to Die organization with helpful resources on self-deliverance and assisted dying for sick folks https://finalexitnetwork.org/

vital roles in our society, the work that involves care, like social work, teaching, domestic work, and personal care assistance, are some of the most poorly paid—and disproportionately women, other gender-oppressed people and/or people of color. This dynamic and our dysfunctional, profit-driven healthcare system are a direct result of the systematic oppression of non-white healers, particularly those from Black and Indigenous communities.

In *Doing Harm: The Truth About How Bad Medicine and Lazy Science Leave Women Dismissed, Misdiagnosed, and Sick*[23], author Maya Dusenbury writes that from the colonial era into the late eighteenth century in the United States, women were the primary healers.

Called "root and herb" doctors, they often combined passed-down medical knowledge from Europe and Africa with knowledge of local medicinal plants as learned from Native American healers. As Dusenberry explains, in the 19th century, "regular" doctors, who were mostly white men, and worked based on medical theory (promoting practices like bloodletting) rather than generations of practical wisdom, sought to professionalize healing into a commodity that could be bought and sold.

Women were part of the Popular Health Movement, which initially opposed the idea of a medical profession, but some women eventually pushed to become "regular" doctors too. When men refused to let women into medical schools, women opened their own.

At the end of the twentieth century, as medicine in Europe was becoming more science-based, medicine in the United States still had relatively few official standards. Seeking to further elevate the profession and eliminate "low-class" competition, the American Medical Association conducted a review of the country's medical schools.

---

23 Maya Dusenbery, Doing Harm: The Truth about How Bad Medicine and Lazy Science Leave Women Dismissed, Misdiagnosed, and Sick (New York: HarperOne, 2019).

The resulting Flexner Report, which concluded that there were too many doctors and too many who were poorly trained, was used to almost totally exclude women and people of color from the medical field for several decades. Dusenberry writes, "By 1915, the portion of medical school graduates who were women had declined to an all-time low of 2.9 percent. Most of the women's and Black medical schools had closed. By 1930 only one women's school remained. The new requirement that all applicants have two years of college education ensured that a medical education was accessible only to the upper classes."

As medicine became monopolized by white men, and something practiced for money, healing became less accessible and more homogenous. Simultaneously, generations of healing knowledge were erased. Today, we are left with an allopathic paradigm that even many doctors admit is extremely limited and causes harm for healthcare workers and patients alike. The systems we're up against and trying to survive in are exhausting and depleting by design. It will take lots of time, intention, and effort over generations to build new systems. Thankfully, there is still healing to be found in community and collective action, right now.

We're Not Meant to Be Isolated

Despite being more technologically connected than ever before, with more opportunities to connect even if bed-bound, most spoonies will tell you that they have struggled with feeling alone. These are scary times to be alive, and a lot of us feel isolated and unsafe. Many of us are without community, spiritually bereft, and disconnected from our own internal wisdom.

That is all compounded by what political scientist and professor Robert D. Putnam describes in his book *Bowling Alone* as the decline of social capital, the very fabric of our connections with each other.[24]

---

24 Robert D. Putnam, Bowling Alone: Revised and Updated: The Collapse and Revival of American Community (Simon & Schuster, Incorporated, 2020).

Almost every client I've ever worked with cited a desire for more community.

My best friend and I constantly fantasize about living in a village, with mutual systems of support, and elders to consult with. It used to be the norm—and still is in some parts of the world—that if you were struggling, in body or mind, that your community, your village, your religious community, community elders, and/or your extended family took care of you.

Many people in the U.S. today are siloed and expected to thrive as independent beings, capable of giving themselves everything they need. I know in my own journey I had a lot of shame around asking for support because I thought I should be able to take care of myself, or somehow come up with the money to pay for the care and help I needed.

When my own family of origin wasn't available, and there weren't other folks around who could naturally fill a caretaking role, I felt a lot of despair, and like I must be failing in some way. In fact, our dominant culture around care and wellness was failing me.

The American pull-yourself-up-by-your-bootstraps narrative is part of what keeps us from experiencing collective health and freedom as well as individual healing. When people don't have success with the healing protocols suggested to them, doctors and healers will blame it on the patient. This happens in public forums, individual doctor's offices, the kitchen table, and everywhere in between.

Many patients are left assuming that something must be wrong with them. In fact, while not explicitly, they're being asked to take on generations worth of systemic oppression all by themselves. Drinking celery juice and exercising every day might benefit your physiology, but it won't change the impact of pollution, white supremacy, income inequality, and the capitalist-informed culturally reinforced busy-holism that causes disease. Financial inaccessibility and the structural barriers to health are huge failings of the wellness industry today.

The hyper-individualistic approach to healing is also shame-y, exclusive, and traumatic in itself. In the context of Black mental health, writer, scholar, and faith worker Zaynab Shahar calls this phenomenon "bootstrap wellness theory." In a May 2019 essay published by the Black Youth Project, she writes, "Meritocracy is a myth and individual hard work isn't enough to overcome structural barriers and achieve socio-economic ascension. Nor should a specific notion of achievement be a factor in someone's worth to the community."[25] Biologically, we are designed for interdependence, not independence. The popular narrative of "going it alone" causes great suffering and severely limits our ability to organize, come together, and make change. The breakdown of communities and the rise of hyper independence has been reinforced by globalization and online connectedness.

Canadian changemaker and founder of Marketing for Hippies, Tad Hargrave writes about the problem this way: "...globalization has not resulted in more togetherness. It has resulted in more individualization. It has created more highly niched communities of affinity and [fewer] communities of geography. Globalization is not, and has never been, a network of highly interconnected villages. It has, and will forever be, the end of villages."[26] He argues that our penchant for rugged individualism severely limits our social change movements because change requires deep community ties, and folks being resourced enough to take action consistently. We've focused for so long on breaking down the social structures that don't serve us without building, or often even envisioning, new support structures to replace them—and the personal and collective resources we need to build them.

25 Zaynab Shahar, "Black Liberation Requires Making Room for Uncomfortable Manifestations of Mental Illness," The Black Youth Project, May 3, 2019, http://blackyouthproject.com/black-liberation-requires-making-room-for-uncomfortable-manifestations-of-mental-illness/.

26 Tad Hargrave, "On Village-Making: The Means and the Ends of Our Personal and Collective Redemption," On Village-Making: The Means and the Ends of Our Personal and Collective Redemption (On Culture Making, December 6, 2022), https://tadhargrave.substack.com/p/on-village-making-the-means-and-the.

In my work and in my community, I've seen a steep rise in physical and mental illness among younger folks, particularly since the 2016 election. It feels like a byproduct of our collective loneliness and a deep feeling of helplessness in the face of the cannibalistic and oppressive culture that has always been here but has now been laid bare for all to see. Racist and bigoted presidents are nothing new, but the election of Donald J. Trump and the subsequent rise of white supremacist movements in the years since has highlighted for a lot of people (especially privileged white folks) just how broken our country is. Coming to terms with that, as well as the climate crisis, is extraordinarily painful. So, it's not surprising that our youth are struggling, and that the struggle is showing up in their bodies. A lot of us don't have obvious places, relationships, or mechanisms to help us process the fear, grief, and other feelings churned up in this upheaval. And when the fear and other feelings remain unprocessed, we get sick(er). It doesn't help that many of the popularized approaches to healing these challenges are also individual rather than collective.

As Hargrave writes:

> We are left with psychological practices of 'self-regulating' of our nervous systems, a triage-like practice that can pull people through an overwhelming crisis by pulling them ever deeper into themselves and by disconnecting and detaching from the world. Self-regulation is not the end all and be all. There are those in the field of psychology pointing at research that shows how the jangled nervous systems of humans are best regulated with the presence and support of other humans, eye-contact, touch, listening, playing together, this sort of co-regulation seems to be more aligned with our neurobiology. Self-regulation is deified because our culture deifies the Self and its independence. It's deified because our culture worships heroes not villages. Self-regulation is seen as a sign of how incredibly

strong and resilient we are. Self-regulation helps us survive but that doesn't mean it's healthy. It just keeps us from dying.

When we're isolated, we feel the pain of not having the community we'd love to take care of us. We also suffer collectively from not having others to care for, or not feeling capable of caring for others. When we aren't connected to community, it's easy to lose sight of the big picture—that humans are resilient and together we can overcome so much—and become deeply discouraged.

We may think things like, "Nobody gets it," "This must be my fault," or "*I* have to find a way to fix this," and our energy stays there. We feel disempowered, seek short-term solutions to ease our suffering, and often blame ourselves—because that's what our dominant culture socializes us to do. My sickest clients, for instance, the ones in the most pain, are also the meanest to themselves.

Why are we so hard on ourselves? Is that just the human condition? If we're looking at nature versus nurture, they're both at play. Your amygdala, part of the limbic system and the part of your brain responsible for perceiving and prepping for emergency events, will definitely tell you that you're stupid, ugly, and incompetent in service of protecting you from the unknown, or perceived harm.

But there's also a significant amount of social conditioning that contributes to self-hatred, and it's worse for folks who have experienced more oppression, and/or have been victims of assault, abuse, neglect, war, and other trauma.

For example, folks who are Black, Indigenous, disabled, fat, or otherwise othered in our society tend to have even more internalized oppression that can show up as even more self-criticism and loathing. This self-hatred can cause us to retreat into ourselves, further exacerbating our own suffering and pulling our energy out of the collective.

Even a small step towards community, being seen by others, we can realize we don't have to do it alone—that healing is really something we do together. Next, I want to explore why your healing is a contribution to the collective, and later, how you can directly connect to that collective with lessons from the healing justice and disability justice movements.

Healing Is a Contribution

"...trauma and healing aren't just private experiences. Sometimes trauma is a collective experience, in which case our approaches for mending must be collective and communal as well."

—Resmaa Menakem

"Love and justice are not two. Without inner change, there can be no outer change; without collective change, no change matters."

—Rev. angel Kyodo williams

Here I want to look at how choosing to heal at an individual level supports our collective liberation, and how choosing to heal in community doubles the effect on both your personal healing and our collective healing.

I encounter a lot of doubt with clients when I affirm that the best thing they can do to change the world is to focus on their healing—in whatever way that manifests for them. As I've mentioned, I struggled with this doubt myself for many years, which contributed to me burning out multiple times. Especially since a lot of my clients identify as changemakers, the worry of not doing enough comes up a lot. Pretty much every person I've supported as a coach has struggled with feeling "worthless," "without a purpose," or like they aren't stepping up enough when they must shift most of their attention and energy toward their healing. It's such a common experience, especially in our culture, where so much value is placed on what we *do* and what we *have* rather than who we *are* and how we are *being*.

If you're not already there, my hope is that you get to a place where you value yourself as you are, regardless of what you can do. For most of us raised in this culture, embracing this concept wholeheartedly can be a journey. Even in writing this, I'm coming off of a couple weeks of going back and forth about how I might volunteer to swing the 2018 election the way I want it to go. I'm asking myself, "Do I really have the spoons to phone bank for the local congressional candidate? Am I letting down my fellow Americans if I don't?"

I'm lucky that I am well enough to even have that internal debate. That's new for me. During the 2016 campaign, I was down for the count. I did a couple hours of phone banking on one good day and that's all I had in me. I had to trust that other people were doing good organizing and mobilizing work. They were, and I am grateful for them.

But whether you're unable to show up for political action, for your work, or to help a chosen family member out, it's easy to worry that you're not doing enough or that you're letting people down. You may have even had that worry before your health challenge(s) emerged, and current circumstances have just exacerbated it. But it's important to understand that beating yourself up for not doing enough does not serve your healing process.

I want to offer another lens that isn't broadcasted widely enough. Investing in your healing is, in itself, a contribution.

It's worth noting that this idea is a little radical—it's not something we typically hear in our culture—but here's how it works:

1. Committing to your healing—physical, mental, emotional, and spiritual—is one of the biggest contributions you can make to society, because healing allows you to show up and be present in a different way. Being on the healing path allows you to be more present to yourself and those around you.

When you are more present to the needs of your own body, it becomes easier for you to heal and take care of yourself. Taking better care of yourself frees up your attention to be more present with other humans, the Earth, and non-human beings around you.

The promise of personal healing is deeper connection, and the more of that we have going on in the human population, the less harm is done, and the more magic we can make together.

2. Choosing to heal subverts the predominant societal norms of putting work, country, and others before your own needs, like caring for your physical and mental health. In this way, choosing to heal is anti-capitalist.

It's important to remember that the current chronic illness epidemic is born out of our capitalist system, as I covered earlier. Makers of highly lucrative drugs that treat rheumatoid arthritis and Crohn's disease,[27] for example, do not have any interest in doctors teaching their patients how to cure themselves.

There is also a widely held belief in the Lyme community that special interests are to blame for the lack of effective treatment options for Lyme disease in the United States.[28] Most chronic illnesses are only chronic because our capitalist healthcare system perpetuates them, in how disease is treated, managed, and studied.

---

27 The first and sixth best selling drugs in 2018 were Humira, used to treat Crohn's disease and Enbrel, which is used to treat rheumatoid arthritis and other conditions. https://www.genengnews.com/a-lists/top-15-best-selling-drugs-of-2018/

28 This is explained in the 2008 documentary "Under Our Skin" and the 2015 sequel, "Under Our Skin 2: Emergence."

Some patients and doctors argue that this is intentional. Even if that's not true, the failure to study certain diseases, and the failure to study the effects of drugs on populations like pregnant women, trans people, and women in general, certainly causes harm.

Furthermore, a lot of information on how to heal, or even cure disease, has been lost, obscured, written off as bogus, or intentionally withheld. So, when you're given a chronic diagnosis, or told that you cannot be healed, and you choose to heal anyway, you're subverting the norms of the Medical Industrial Complex and giving the middle finger to enterprises that profit from keeping us unwell.

This supports our collective resistance to structures of oppression and our reclamation of power.

3. In the Shambhala Buddhist tradition, fearlessness is considered a form of generosity because by being fearless, you give others permission to be fearless too. Prioritizing your own healing is generous because it sets a powerful example for others and gives them permission to focus on their healing too.

    Some people will see you taking care of yourself and freak out. Their inner critic will wonder, "Who do you think *you* are, spending time on healing?" That's just their societal programming talking. It's not about you. Part of the reason this whole healing thing is so hard is that so many people feel like they have to hide their illness, pain, and other struggles. When it's all under the radar, we have no idea how many people are in the same boat as us, and we miss out on the opportunity to support each other.

By choosing to heal and sharing our process, more healing can happen in community.

4. Prioritizing personal healing supports the paradigm of healing-centered changemaking, rather than reinforcing the aggressive "fight, fight, fight," "us vs. them," "work as hard as you possibly can until you can't," style of changemaking. In this paradigm, sometimes the change agents begin to resemble the very people and institutions they're fighting against. I'll say more about this next in the Learning from Healing Justice and Disability Justice chapter in Section 3.

5. Healing is a contribution to your lineage—your ancestors and your descendants. By choosing to heal, you will be healing ancestral trauma in your body that has been passed down to you by your family of origin and your community. Think about the impacts of war, domestic violence, genocide, racism, slavery, and addiction.

All that trauma lives in our cells. Every family has trauma in their lineage, and it's likely that many of your ancestors did not have the opportunity to do a lot of healing. When you do your own healing work, you are realizing unsung dreams that your ancestors had for their descendants. And, whether or not you choose to have your own children, choosing to heal your trauma is a huge contribution to the next generations. All that trauma you heal is trauma that you don't act out on others and don't pass on.

6. More healing means more love. Choosing to heal—whether that means working towards curing something, accepting what is, spiritual transformation, or something else—will allow you to experience more joy and love others from a full heart. This is because healing requires us to work towards loving all of ourselves, telling the truth to ourselves, and practicing self-compassion at an especially high level. I'll say more about how to do this in Section 3.

   When we love ourselves unconditionally like that, we can't help but see ourselves in others. Suddenly we are able to see the soft and squishy humanity in even the most outwardly deplorable individuals.

7. Healing asks us to live in alignment, with our own truths and the fundamental truths of the living world. This is also referred to as living in right relationship. Living in right relationship asks us to stand up for the wellbeing and freedom of all, including the Earth, other humans, and all living beings. Moving more people to live in right relationship is the most necessary task of these times. As a society we have been misaligned since the first colonizers set foot on Turtle Island, and we are suffering the consequences.

   Now, we are living through a great collective reckoning in the United States, with some fighting to keep the old ways of being entrenched, and others working to build a new paradigm altogether. More and more people are standing up to injustice because they are no longer willing to tolerate living in such a misaligned society; one that doesn't value all human lives equitably and makes it hard for us as individuals to live in alignment with what we know to be true in our bones.

NOËLLE JANKA

We've had enough of the needless suffering and want to
build equity and healing into our culture and institutions.
The way we will achieve that is by coming back to our own
humanity and doing what we can to remain connected to
ourselves, the Earth, and each other.

Pause here and take a moment to reflect. How might your healing
journey be a contribution to:
- Your community?
- Your family, ancestors, and descendants?
- This country?
- The Earth and other living beings?

Record your thoughts in your healing journal if you wish.

Healing is also a contribution when it becomes a vehicle for building community and community power. In her 1998 book, *Medicine
Stories: History, Culture, and the Politics of Integrity*,[29] Puerto Rican
Jewish author and poet Aurora Levins Morales writes that "Healing
takes place in community, in the telling and bearing of witness, in the
naming of trauma and in the grief and rage and defiance that follow."
Part of what Morales is pointing to here is how healing with others not
only makes it easier for us to heal individually but brings us together,
a first step in building powerful movements.

To quote Johanna Hedva again, "The most anti-capitalist protest is
to care for another and to care for yourself. To take on the historically
feminized and therefore invisible practice of nursing, nurturing, caring.
To take seriously each other's vulnerability and fragility and precarity,
and to support it, honor it, empower it. To protect each other, to

---

29 Aurora Levins Morales, Medicine Stories History, Culture and the Politics of Integrity (Cambridge, Mass: South
End Press, 2000).

enact and practice community. A radical kinship, an interdependent sociality, a politics of care."[30]

There is a deep longing in our population for connection and community. If we are courageous and willing to say "yes" to it, and willing to be open and vulnerable with each other, we can create the connection we crave. One of the most heart-warming and empowering events I've ever attended was an open mic for people with Lyme disease.

I was just an audience member but I have never felt as seen and included as I did in that room, crying and laughing with so many other people who shared the depth of my most painful experiences. We need community to heal, individually and collectively. This is why I proselytize so much about cultivating support networks and being open with people about our health challenges (for more on how to do this, see the Build a Support Dream Team in Section 3).

By coming together to share our personal and collective longings and the gifts of our healing journeys, even from our individual couches or beds, we can build and strengthen our communities, and create change together. What's incredible is that despite all that is working against us, we still have agency. We can interrupt cycles of trauma and oppression at the personal level and collective level, and it's already happening. The body is always trying to heal itself, and culture is constantly shifting and changing.

The rise in attention on anti-racism and eradicating police brutality after the murders of George Floyd, Breonna Taylor, Ahmaud Arbaury and other Black individuals, showed us that rapid culture change is possible when a foundation for change has been crafted. We have WAY more work to do to end state violence and unlearn white supremacy culture, especially as the cultural backlash to this progress grows. And the protests of 2020 and 2021, the previous five years of protesting and organizing in Ferguson, Missouri and elsewhere, and

---

30 Johanna Hedva, "Sick Woman Theory," 2020, https://johannahedva.com/SickWomanTheory_Hedva_2020.pdf.

nearly 200 years of civil rights organizing before that, have brought us to where we are today.

A lot of people have been doing a lot of deep change work for a long time. It's up to us to carry the torch, keep building community, keep organizing, and bring our healing into justice movements. And contrary to popular belief, there are so many more options than protesting. I highly recommend the list, "26 ways to be in the struggle, beyond the streets (June 2020 update)," available on the Disability Visibility Project website.[31]

The more we can bring focused attention and intention to our personal and collective healing, the more successful we'll be in realizing the results we want on a systemic level. We can build a different economic system that isn't rooted in exploitation and a healthcare system that actually helps people heal. We can write healing-centered public policy, with the most impacted individuals at the head of the table. We can and we should.

And, to ensure that we are not perpetuating the harm we are trying to heal in this process, we each need to do our own internal healing work too. Part of why this is so critical is because our bodies are not just our own. We are part of a collective consciousness and collective body. Somatic therapist Tada Hozumi explained the connection to me like this when we spoke in January 2019:[32]

> I see cultures as bodies as well. So, when groups of people come together we have our local bodies which [are] individual bodies that we can feel and sense into. Then there's an unconscious field where there's a larger body that integrates all the bodies that are connected. That body is still a body. We can't see it, but it still has a nervous system but it's unseen, but we're connected

---

31 Alice Wong, "26 Ways to Be in the Struggle, beyond the Streets (June 2020 Update)," Disability Visibility Project, December 26, 2020, https://disabilityvisibilityproject. com/2020/06/06/26-ways-to-be-in-the-struggle-beyond-the-streets-june-2020-update/.

32 Tada Hozumi, zoom conversation with the author, January 2019.

to it. So, it's kind of like a Matrix deal and I think when we're talking about healing trauma in movement spaces, the thing I want to really put forward is that what we call justice is actually the healing of that larger cultural body. And it's still a body. That's the point. It's still a body. This larger thing has a nervous system, that has thoughts, has feelings, it's a being, and they are a body. So, the methods that are going to work to heal that body are methods of somatic healing and that's why it's so important. So, when we understand how to heal our bodies we start to learn how to heal the larger cultural body. You can't do one without the other…you cannot separate the individual from the collective healing of bodies; it's impossible. So, if you're talking about healing let's say cancer you can't disconnect that from healing colonialism. That's the ludicrous [situation] we're in is that we don't actually connect the two, but it's absolutely important. It also means that political movements and social justice, absolutely for [them] to be effective, have to be trauma based. In my perspective it's unethical when it's not. And the reason why is because the thing that you're trying to facilitate the healing of and change of is a body. And so when you don't treat it as a body or even see it as a body, but are not treating it in a trauma-informed lens you're bringing in the potential of it being retraumatized. So, then the same patterns are starting to repeat and that's how oppression propagates.

When part of our collective body is experiencing trauma, we are all affected by that. Conversely, as we work together on collective healing, all our individual bodies benefit. Hozumi writes that "…our individual and collective healing are inseparable—because oppression is trauma and trauma is oppression. When there is trauma from violence in our relationships, it becomes held in cultural somas as systemic oppression. And vice versa, when there is unaddressed systemic oppression held in cultural somas, it manifests as traumatizing violence in our relationships."[33]

The visual that follows illustrates this connection between our institutions and culture, our collective nervous system, and our individual nervous systems. Systems and culture shaped by kyriarchy, which includes intersecting patterns of domination like colonialism, patriarchy, racial capitalism, and white supremacy, perpetrate oppression and violence on the collective. This creates both collective and personal trauma, which is felt both in the personal and collective soma and nervous systems.

This trickle-down pattern of trauma is illustrated by the arrow and flag on the left side of the visual. Conversely, healing trauma in the nervous system at the individual level, which includes healing internalized oppression, allows us to participate in and support the wellbeing of the collective nervous system. A more regulated collective nervous system (made up of more regulated and resilient individuals) builds collective resiliency to transform our systems and uproot the oppression that lives within them. This trickle-up process is depicted by the arrow and flag on the right side of the visual. Currently there is much more oppression and violence in our culture than there is healing. As we enroll others to join us on the healing path, we can work together to tip the balance towards healing.

I call this the Heal It Up approach to making change. If you've spent time in activist spaces or attended marches or demonstrations, you are familiar with the rallying cry to "Burn It Down." Yes, we need to dismantle the systems and institutions that oppress us, and, after generations of our humanity being ground down, we need to build our collective foundation in order to effectively facilitate change. We are lucky to be in a cultural moment when there is more interest in personal healing. More and more people are trying to figure out how

---

33 Tada Hozumi, Selfish Activist, accessed July 17, 2019, https://web.archive.org/web/20201201205032/https://selfishactivist.com/.

to live well in this wildly unwell world. There is an opportunity to also bring them into a wider understanding of the causes of our unwellness and the need for more politicized and contextualized healing solutions.

The "Heal It Up" Approach To Making Social Change

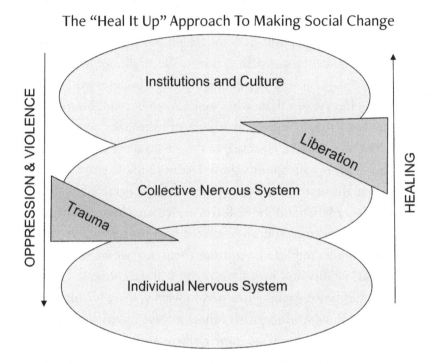

While it's still woefully inadequate and mostly devoid of context, access to mental health and alternative health services *is* expanding, and more people, especially young people, are pursuing healing support. There are also more and more trauma-informed, politicized healers coming on the scene as more healers can access needed training and connect with healers in other disciplines and with other cultural backgrounds.

As you reach the close of this chapter, I hope that you feel closer to believing the reality that you are always healing yourself and society at the same time. I look forward to the day when we are having more conversations about our collective wellness and how to design our communities and institutions to center wellbeing.

Spoonies and disabled individuals are uniquely qualified to provide vital expertise and leadership in this realm because we have had to learn how to survive in systems that weren't designed to support us. We've had to figure out how to reclaim our joy, connection, and aliveness in a society that doesn't value it. We might not lead protests, attend lobby days, or lead organizing meetings, because we don't have the spoons, but we can share what we know to be true about healing. And that has a bigger impact than most of us realize.

We have a lot to offer, especially to those who aren't already thinking about healing. As your spoons allow, I want to invite you to consider how you might share your healing process for collective benefit. Just as Black Lives Matter and the #MeToo movements have amplified and elevated national conversations centered in truth-telling, we need to be having a louder public conversation about how we are being denied our physical vitality and how we can and will reclaim it.

This could start by telling one person what you are learning as you read this book, or working with others to heal internalized patterns of domination so that you are more resilient and connected in efforts to dismantle external systems of harm. It could also look like lending your expertise as a spoonie to support more able-bodied individuals in an organization or collective to be more inclusive and more accessible.

We all have a place in the movement and there are many ways to contribute.[34] If this feels intimidating, know that your role and how you uniquely contribute will become clear. As you continue on the healing path and take steps to deprogram yourself, you will naturally move through the world in different ways, connect more deeply to

---

34 When helping clients identify their gifts and place in change work, I like referencing Deepa Iyer's Social Change Ecosystem Map which offers nine roles that one can pursue to engage in social change efforts for equity, liberation, justice, and equity more collaboratively, sustainably, and effectively. Learn more in Iyer's guidebook, Social Change Now: A Guide for Reflection and Connection and at https://www.socialchangemap.com/framework, accessed 1/16/2023

your authenticity, and see new opportunities to join others in dreaming and creating a more just and supportive world.

Reflection Questions:

I suggest you pause here and tune into your own vision for wellbeing for yourself and for the collective. Reflect on the following questions and record some notes in your healing journal if you like:

- What kind of healing experience would you love to have? What kind of support would you love in your healing? Who, in your wildest dreams, is offering that support? What would you be able to do in your life with this kind of healing support?
- What do you wish the narrative and social expectations around healing were like in this country? What would they sound like? Who would be sharing them?
- What do you want healthcare in this country to look like and feel like for you and others? What is present? What is not present?
- How does this vision for healthcare help us all get free more broadly? How does it change America?

Deprogramming Ourselves

"People thought of revolution chiefly in terms of taking state power. But we've had revolutions, and we've seen how the states which they have created have turned out to be like replicas of the states which they opposed. You have to bring those two words together and recognize that we are responsible for the evolution of the human species. It's a question of two-sided transformation and not just the oppressed versus the oppressor. We have to change ourselves in order to change the world."

—Grace Lee Boggs

"Imperialism leaves behind germs of rot which we must clinically detect and remove from our land but from our minds as well."

—Frantz Fanon

Now that we've reviewed some societal causes of our collective unwellness and the power of collective action, in this chapter I want to say more about how to use that information to support your healing and the healing of those around you. In my own healing journey and in supporting many clients with health challenges and various types of trauma, I've observed three major benefits of bringing attention to one's place in the collective context:

1. Remembering and feeling your place in the collective can help you feel less alone with your (health) challenges.
2. Understanding how you have been influenced by societal programming can allow you to heal the resulting trauma and

detrimental patterns, in turn allowing you to reclaim some of your wellbeing. I refer to this as "deprogramming."

3. The practice of seeing yourself in the collective context naturally leads you to be more community-oriented, interdependent, and loving to those around you.

I'll share more about each of these benefits below.

1. Remembering and feeling your place in the collective can help you feel less alone with your (health) challenges.

Healing can easily become an isolating experience and it's not unusual for feelings of loneliness to actually cause more suffering than the illness, injury, addiction, or whatever it is you're healing. It is common to get caught up in feeling like you're the only one suffering, and it's not fair that you have to work so hard on your healing while everyone else appears to be gallivanting about. I have experienced a lot of this!

But this propensity toward feeling isolated is propelled by the aforementioned societal worship of individualism and chronic loneliness in our society. Even when we aren't alone, many of us feel deeply lonely. But this experience, however widespread, is not actually reflective of the truth, which is that we are never really alone—neither physically alone nor alone in our experience.

Even if we are the only human in a room or a frozen tundra, we are surrounded by other beings and we are being held by the Earth. We are not alone in our experience because at any given time, many, many people are sick and suffering (mostly outside the public eye) and going through the same things we're going through. When we can remember that, it can ease or totally freeze the "I'm the only one, I'm so alone" mind chatter.

Then we can turn our attention toward feeling ourselves in the web of individuals and communities who are also suffering at the hands of our toxic culture, and perhaps also on the healing path. Feeling into these connections can bring a real felt sense of peace and even joy. I'll offer a practice for energetically connecting with others who are suffering in Section 3, Disconnect and Reconnect.

2. Understanding how you have been influenced by societal programming can allow you to heal the resulting trauma and detrimental patterns, in turn allowing you to reclaim some of your well being.

   Seeing yourself in context is great because it allows you to see that just because you live in a messy, toxic society, you are not a mess. You can begin to cleanse yourself of the toxicity and chart your own healing path. This cleansing process, what I call "deprogramming," is a practice of reclaiming your humanity and connection to other beings.

   This begins by identifying and releasing kyriarchal social programming that you learned from your family of origin, your community, the media, and other cultural, religious, and government institutions. Regardless of our race, class, or privilege, we have all absorbed kyriarchal social programming, and most of us have been made to believe that we have to play the game according to dominant culture's rules in order to survive—both to meet our basic needs and gain social acceptance. Most of us also aren't presented with a lot of alternatives. The notion of "living off the grid" simply isn't accessible to many. So, most of us do play by the rules, even if the rules are harming us.

Committing to deprogramming will allow you to heal health challenges with more ease because it involves cleansing your-self of oppressive thought patterns that contributed to your unwellness in the first place. This process gives you space to observe your thoughts and make different choices about your behavior. This might look like realizing that you have a belief that you have to work 50 hours a week, then seeing that you're only getting paid for 40 hours and that no one actu-ally asked you to work extra, so it would probably be okay to scale back.

Being able to create this separation and see that you have choices also means you can choose to live according to what you know to be true in your own heart and body, and act in ways that support your personal and our collective wellbeing. Living in deeper alignment frees up the body to heal more easily because you are no longer consciously or unconsciously doing lots of things that don't work for you.

As I said above, alignment is foundational to what healing really is: aligning your actions to what is most healing for yourself, the human community, the Earth, and all beings. If you work on healing your body but continue to mindlessly perpetuate and uphold systems of oppression, you are likely to become ill again, and limit the healing of others.

I want to highlight that bringing attention to internalized kyriarchy isn't about being a victim and blaming all your issues on outside forces. It's actually about you empowering yourself to dismantle oppression and tap into our collective healing capability as a society. It's convenient for institutions that benefit from our disempowerment for us to believe that our illness or pain is our fault.

As long as we're caught up in blaming ourselves—or perhaps questioning our sanity because our doctors or therapists can't find answers for us—we're stuck in a sort of liminal zone where we aren't present to the collective context or seeing how powerful and resilient, we still are. Deprogramming allows you to reclaim your agency and see that you are extraordinarily powerful and capable of achieving great things—including healing.

3. The practice of seeing yourself in the collective context naturally leads you to be more community-oriented, interdependent, and loving to those around you. Staying present to the collective context in your own healing also supports our collective healing. The more we are aware of oppressive systems, constructs, and ideas, and how we have personally been harmed by them and benefited from them, the more effectively we can dismantle them, choose not to perpetuate them, and therefore inflict less harm on ourselves and others. For example, if you're working class and white, you have experienced oppression as a low-income person, but have also benefited from being white, even if you haven't been conscious of it. Owning and understanding the identities you hold, and how those identities impact your actions, is an important first step in undoing all the aspects of kyriarchy. When we understand the identities we hold and the roles we play, we can choose how we want to be with them.

For example, not-yet-disabled people can see that they have able-bodied privilege, *choose* to be anti-ableist, and educate themselves about how to meet different access needs.

Deprogramming has many different layers. You may feel like you're making progress deprogramming internalized racism, and then become conscious of a whole bunch of fat-shaming material in your psyche. The more you pay attention, the more programming you'll find, related to whiteness, ableism, and patriarchy, and the list goes on. Deprogramming, like the wider healing journey, is a process and something that doesn't have an endpoint.

It is a lifelong practice, and one that's worth treating with as much gentleness as rigor. Over time, as you become more and more aware of programming that lives within you, you will be able to shift your behavior so that it is in line with what you actually believe. For example if you believe that all people should be treated with love, dignity, and respect, being in the practice of deprogramming might allow you to more consistently act that way in your own life, which might include voicing your opposition against oppressive policies; organizing for equitable policy; noticing and stopping yourself before making a microaggression; and/or participating in mutual aid with individuals most harmed by the status quo.

I will say more about *how* to deprogram yourself in the Train Your Brain chapter and suggest that you be on the lookout for opportunities to explore and examine your relationship to kyriarchy given the identities you hold. For example, if you're an owning class person in white body, you might seek out courses on class privilege and anti-racism. If you're a trans person of color, you might look for supportive spaces designed for individuals who also hold those identities, such as a trans-affirming counseling group led by a BIPOC therapist.

Most spoonies benefit tremendously from learning more about ableism so that they can better see where it shows up in their lives and when their actions might be informed by internalized ableism. I want to invite you to consider what kind of support you'd love for your deprogramming work. It can be pretty intense so it's helpful to have people to process with.

Perhaps you want to enroll a friend to be an accountability buddy. Maybe you want to start an anti-ableist reading group or a racial healing support group, or even hire a coach to support you in your process. We all need to do this work, so if you worry about asking people to be in it with you, remember that support will be a gift to them too.

If while reading this you experience shame, please know that it's okay to pause and attend to that feeling. Wrap yourself in a blanket. Talk to a friend. Write about what you're experiencing and know that all is well. That is a common reaction to delving into deprogramming work. That feeling will arise, but it won't be constant, and learning to be with it and move through it is part of the process. You are not alone in having thoughts that aren't aligned with your beliefs. You are not a bad person. We ALL have kyriarchal narratives to deprogram.

The more we understand the big picture of oppression and how we have internalized it, the more easily we can place ourselves in it, resist it, and reclaim our personal and collective power. My hope is that by seeing the big picture more clearly, you will feel empowered to be courageous in your own healing, support others with theirs, and help dream up and build a robust movement for the just systems we need to heal.

Reflection Questions:

- What are you noticing/feeling in your body after reading this section?
- What kind of support would you love to deprogram the kyriarchal narratives that live in your body and mind? What might make the process easier or sweeter for you?
- If you've already done some deprogramming work, e.g. anti-racist work, what feels like the next area for you to explore?

Learning from Healing Justice and Disability Justice

"By centering the leadership of those most impacted, we keep ourselves grounded in real-world problems and find creative strategies for resistance."
—Sins Invalid's 10 Principles of Disability Justice

We have talked about how individual healing can be a contribution to collective liberation because it makes us more compassionate, connected, and resilient. Here I want to share more about how individual healing, when practiced in relationship to collective healing, can be a foundation for systems change.

The need for bringing a healing-centered, trauma-informed, and access-expanding lens to collective change work is becoming more apparent and more widely accepted thanks to the queer, BIPOC-led healing justice and disability justice movements.

This chapter provides a brief introduction to these movements and resources for further exploration. Informed by the most marginalized among us, as well as seasoned front-line healers and activists, the narratives of these two movements offer us a new standard for what just care could and should look like, in the United States and beyond. These movements also offer invaluable guidance about how we need to be with each other as we are advocating for and building the care networks and institutions we dream of.

In the same way that getting more people on the healing path supports our collective physical, mental, and spiritual wellbeing, bringing a healing focus into change work supports the wellbeing, longevity, and success of our social change movements. Bringing healing into changemaking work makes our movements safer, as well as more inviting, accessible, sustainable, and resilient—and therefore more successful.

I wish I had understood that when I was a young organizer. I want to cry thinking about the harm I caused when I was an angry, exhausted, and burned-out twenty-something. I made messes that I still regret. And it hurts to see that my experience is one small part of a few generations-worth of burnt out and distracted changemakers making messes in movement work. We need empowered, compassionate leaders who are doing their healing work and can help others do the same.

In "A Not So Brief Personal History of the Healing Justice Movement,"[35] writer, culture worker, performance artist, and disability/ transformative justice worker Leah Lakshmi Piepzna-Samarasinha, describes the prevailing problem in our social justice movements so well:

> Most folks I know come to activist spaces longing to heal. But our movements are often more filled with ableism and burnout than they are full of healing. We work and work and work from a place of crisis. Healing is seen as irrelevant, just for folks with money, an individual responsibility, something you do on your own time. Our movements are so burnout paced, with little to no room for grief, anger, trauma, spirituality, disability, aging, parenting, or sickness, that many people leave them when we age, have kids, get sick(er) or more disabled, or just can't make it to twelve meetings a week anymore.

Social and environmental change leaders often bring their internalized oppression and trauma into their changemaking work, recreating all the same dynamics inside their groups that they are hoping to change outside their groups. A lot of changemaking work has been rooted in

---

35 Leah Lakshmi Piepzna-Samarasinha, "A Not-so-Brief Personal History of the Healing Justice Movement, 2010–2016," TransformHarm.org, accessed February 1, 2023, https://transformharm.org/ hj_resource/a-not-so-brief-personal-history-of-the-healing-justice-movement-2010-2016/.

anger about the current state of affairs but rather than processing the anger, we have acted on it and let it guide our work.

There's a lot to be mad about. And though the anger is valid, and can be an effective motivator, anger usually doesn't keep people doing social change work for the long haul. Without thoughtful containers for healing, rest, and connection, the anger and aggression take a lot of energy to sustain, and breed exhaustion over time.

The language of social movements is often rooted in aggression and scarcity, the same things we are looking to dismantle in our activist work. We frequently hear about "the fight" for that, or "the struggle" for this, or being "against" something. When what we're wanting is love—of all people, of the planet, of all beings everywhere—this aggressive stance alone isn't going to get us there. It's misaligned. Mirroring the systems of oppression we're fighting against is not only ineffective from a social change perspective, but on a personal level it doesn't give us the space we need to heal and change.

I love the way Fania Davis, social justice activist, civil rights trial attorney, restorative justice practitioner, writer, scholar, and Angela Davis' sister, described her own transformation with activism in a "Yes!" magazine interview.[36]

I reached a point where I felt out of balance from all of the anger, the fighting, from a kind of hypermasculine way of being that I had to adopt to be a successful trial lawyer. And also from around 30 years of the hyperaggressive stance that I was compelled to take as an activist—from being against this and against that, and fighting this and fighting that. Intuitively, I realized that I needed an infusion of more feminine and spiritual and creative and healing energies to come back into balance.

---

36 Sarah Van Gelder, "The Radical Work of Healing: Fania and Angela Davis on a New Kind of Civil Rights Activism," Yes! Magazine, https://www.yesmagazine.org/issue/life-after-oil/2016/02/19/the-radical-work-of-healing-fania-and-angela-davis-on-a-new-kind-of-civil-rights-activism.

As I've shared before, when I wasn't committed to my own healing, when I was pushing through my pain, I was a huge jerk. I was meanest to myself, but that showed up in my interactions with others and strained my relationships. I have compassion for myself because it is difficult to be present and authentic with others when you're constantly in agony, *and* expending energy trying to make it seem like you're not in agony. I call this the "I'm fine" approach to living with health challenges.

You might think it's working for you—btdubs, it's not—but it's *really* not working for the people around you, because you're not being authentic and fully present with them. You're showing up as a wall instead of inviting them to be in relationship with you or letting them support you. And deep relationship is necessary for ongoing and effective changemaking.

Because of the work of leaders in the healing justice and disability justice movements like Leah Piepzna-Samarasinha, Naomi Ortiz, Mia Mingus, Alice Wong, Prentis Hemphill, Dr. Diana Quinn, creators of the Healing Histories Project: Cara Page, Susan Raffo, Anjali Taneja; groups like the Fireweed Collective, Healing By Choice, Political Healers, and many others, more social change organizations and even their funders are seeing the necessity of weaving healing into their changemaking work. And here I mean healing in the most holistic sense.

Whether you've been involved in change work or not, most spoonies can benefit tremendously from learning about these movements and the work they have already done to help us understand how we got here—to a reality in which so many people are sick, disabled, and unsupported—and where we can go from here to create different possibilities for ourselves and our communities.

First, let's look at what these movements are about, how they started, and who initiated them.

The **disability justice movement** grew out of and was a reaction to the disability rights movement, which was seen to exclude people who hold multiple marginalized identities. It was conceived by Black, brown, queer, and trans disabled individuals in reaction to their exclusion from the mainstream disability rights movement, which privileged white, male, and straight perspectives.[37]

Disability justice as a term was first coined in 2005 by members of the original Disability Justice Collective, founded in the San Francisco Bay area by Patty Berne, Mia Mingus, Stacey Milbern, Leroy Moore, Eli Clare, and Sebastian Margaret. In *Care Work: Dreaming Disability Justice*, Leah Lakshmi Piepzna-Samarasinha writes of these founders, "Disabled queer and trans Black, Asian, and white activists and artists, they dreamed up a movement-building framework that would center the lives, needs, and organizing strategies of disabled queer and trans and/or Black and brown people marginalized from mainstream disability rights organizing's white-dominated, single issue focus."[38]

Piepzna-Samarasinha also said of disability justice that, "...our focus is less on civil rights legislation as the only solution to ableism and more on a vision of liberation that understands that the state was built on racist, colonialist ableism and will not save us because it was created to kill us."

Activist and singer/songwriter Nomy Lamm has written that, "Disability justice challenges the idea that our worth as individuals has to do with our ability to perform as productive members of society. It insists that our worth is inherent and tied to the liberation of all beings. Like transformative justice, reproductive justice, and environmental justice, it implies a movement-building strategy and an anti-capitalist

---

37 "Disability Justice," Wikipedia (Wikimedia Foundation, November 25, 2022), https://en.wikipedia.org/wiki/Disability_justice.

38 Piepzna-Samarasinha, Leah Lakshmi. "Preface." In Care Work Dreaming Disability Justice. Vancouver, B.C: Arsenal Pulp Press, 2021.

critique."[39] Disability justice reminds us that all bodies are essential and valid and have unique needs that must be honored.[40]

Cultural/memory worker, curator, and organizer Cara Page has said that the modern-day **healing justice movement** is concerned with, "Transforming the consequences of oppression on our bodies, hearts, and minds."[41] She's also said very poignantly that, "Our movements themselves have to be healing, or there's no point to them."[42]

Prioritizing healing in our movements is not a new idea but an old one that we're coming back to. It's also important to understand that the disability justice and healing justice movements, which overlap and intersect, were both started and continue to be led by people of color. Piepzna-Samarasinha writes that "Healing justice as a movement and a term was created by queer and trans people of colour and in particular Black and brown femmes, centering working-class, poor, disabled and Southern/rural healers. Before 'healing justice' was a phrase, healers have been healing folks at kitchen tables and community clinics for a long time—from the acupuncture clinics run by Black Panthers like Mutulu Shakur in North America in the 1960s and 1970s, to our bone-deep Black, Indigenous, people of colour and pre-Christian European traditions of healing with herbs, acupuncture, touch, prayer, and surgery." More specifically, healing justice is a political strategy launched by the Kindred Southern Healing Justice Collective in 2006 "to intervene and respond on generational trauma and systemic oppression, and build community/survivor led responses

---

39 Nomy Lamm, "This Is Disability Justice," The Body Is Not An Apology, September 1, 2015, https://thebodyisnotanapology.com/magazine/this-is-disability-justice/.

40 For a brief and excellent introduction to disability justice and what it means to practice it, I recommend the March 20, 2019 episode of Autumn Brown and adrienne maree brown's podcast How to Survive the End of the World, entitled "Disability Justice of the Apocalypse: Leah Lakshmi Piepzna-Samarsinha Gets Us Together," featuring Leah Lakshmi Piepzna-Samarsinha.

41 "HJ Resources," TransformHarm.org, accessed February 1, 2023, https://transformharm.org/healing-justice/.

42 Leah Lakshmi Piepzna-Samarsinha, "A Not-so-Brief Personal History of the Healing Justice Movement, 2010–2016," TransformHarm.org, accessed February 1, 2023, https://transformharm.org/hj_resource/a-not-so-brief-personal-history-of-the-healing-justice-movement-2010-2016/.

rooted in southern traditions of resiliency to sustain our emotional/
physical/spiritual/psychic and environmental well being."[43]

In her 2022 book, *Liberated to the Bone: Histories. Bodies. Futures,*[44]
writer, cultural worker, and bodyworker Susan Raffo writes,

> When I use the phrase 'healing justice,' I am reflecting on how
> the systems we seek to change outside of our bodies are also
> carried within our bodies. I am recognizing that the systems
> of care in Western medicine that we depend on are also part
> of the systems of dominance and oppression that we want to
> transform. And finally, I recognize that those most impacted
> by systems of dominance and empire building, specifically
> Indigenous, Black and Brown people, have culturally grounded
> systems of care and support that have been and are sometimes
> still being violently attacked, minimized and disappeared, and
> then repackaged and sold by people outside those cultural
> traditions. 'Healing Justice' is more than healing that happens
> to people who care about justice.

Raffo also encourages readers to think of healing justice as a lens,
a felt sense, and a way of knowing in the body; something we can all
access and live into.

The healing justice and disability justice movements grew out of
the need for femme, queer, trans, sick and disabled people of color
to heal personally and together from the near constant trauma per-
petuated by our current systems. White readers please understand:
this movement is not about us. However, I believe healers and sick
and disabled people who do not share the identities listed above can
respectfully learn from and benefit from understanding the brilliance
and strategies of these movements and can work in solidarity with

43 "What Is Healing Justice," KindredSouthernHealingCollective.org, accessed March 3, 2023, https://kindred-southernhjcollective.org/what-is-healing-justice/

44 Susan Raffo, Liberated to the Bone: Histories. Bodies. Futures. (Chico, CA: AK Press, 2022).

healing and disability justice leaders if invited. One of my favorite healing justice principles is "We begin by listening."

When is that ever a bad strategy? I'd argue, rarely. There is always something to be learned. And how often have white people in particular failed to listen? OFTEN. These movements show us that by choosing to show up differently, we can create infinitely more possibilities for more inclusive and effective healing and change.

Both the healing and disability justice movements teach us (or those of us for whom it's not already obvious) that lifting up the voices and minds of the most marginalized communities, and centering their needs, benefits everyone. That is, if we design our organizations and institutions to serve the needs of the most marginalized and most vulnerable—poor, disabled, sick, queer, Black and Indigenous folks— everyone's life will get better as a result because everyone's needs will be met. There will be way less suffering.

When some people are being marginalized, even the most privileged feel the drain of the imbalance—energetically, financially, spiritually, politically, and otherwise. Widespread suffering is also a drain on our institutions, our economy, our knowledge and cultural economies, and other crucial resources. Worse still, when there isn't a seat at the table for everyone in policy-making or other decision-making con- texts, we're missing out on some of the most brilliant and experienced voices in the room.

The most marginalized are often also the most resilient and cre- ative because they are the most practiced in surviving in a world that wasn't designed to include them. Healing justice and disability justice acknowledge that these historically marginalized communities hold the deepest wells of wisdom in our society. And folks with chronic health challenges, regardless of race, class, or other identities they hold, have their own deep wisdom from learning to survive in an environment that often threatens their survival and wellbeing.

Healing justice and disability justice also ask us to do our own internal healing work in service of the collective. As scholar Loretta Pyles describes in the essay *Healing Justice for a World On Fire*,[45] "We can think of healing justice as a kind of balm for the inflammation caused by our egoic self-centeredness, the violence we perpetrate against ourselves and others, and the residue of domination and victimization. It is a framework and set of practices that can help us to uproot what bell hooks calls 'imperialist white supremacist capitalist patriarchy.'"

As I have written already, doing our own personal uprooting—what I refer to as deprogramming—is something that we all need to do. Folks with health challenges are simply being asked to do it with more urgency because of how much it impacts our lives. We got sick in part because we feel the weight of the world a little more than other people, our physical and mental illnesses a symptom of what Charles Eisenstein calls, "The mutiny of the soul."[46] In other words, our health challenges are an outer expression of the soul saying, "This shit is really fucked!!!"

Healing justice encourages us to come as we are and heal in community, perhaps with healing traditions used by our ancestors or, with consent and respect, the healing rituals of someone else's ancestors. Part of what makes the experience of chronic pain and illness so difficult is that our society at large doesn't have traditions or rituals for it—for the people experiencing it, for caregivers, or other people around the sick person.

Our whole relationship to birth, living, illness, and dying in this country is compromised by the dominant cultural understanding that our body is a machine we use to do, achieve, and earn. This is antithetical to everything we intuitively understand about our body's relationship to the rest of our being, to other bodies, and to the Earth.

---

45 Loretta Pyles, "Healing Justice for a World on Fire," The Arrow, December 20, 2018, https://arrow-journal.org/healing-justice-for-a-world-on-fire/.

46 Charles Eisenstein, "Depression, Anxiety and Fatigue: Symptoms of the Mutiny of the Soul," Conscious Reminder, October 12, 2017, https://consciousreminder.com/2017/05/30/mutiny-of-the-soul/.

Healing justice and disability justice help us come back to what we know in our bones to be true about being human and what we need to heal.

You don't have to be part of a healing justice collective or space to start working with healing justice principles. In fact, my dream is that more and more people will start to see societal problems like addiction, sexual harassment, and violence as things that need healing rather than punishment, and that healing rituals and space for healing will become commonplace in all spaces where humans gather, whether it's an activist meeting, a corporate office, a hospital, or the DMV.

I am definitely not the only person with this dream and have tremendous gratitude for the ancestors and current leaders of these movements who work to help us understand our context and heal our way forward together. I appreciate that the healing justice movement acknowledges that no one person or one community's healing will be the same. It will look very different in different places depending on the needs of those involved.

Pyles writes:

> Healing justice looks different for everyone, depending on their life history, personality, and social location. It may mean attending to and working with the systemic roots of psycho-social issues such as addiction, anxiety, and depression, or it may mean learning about and taking action on issues of social justice and inclusivity in the workplace or in spiritual communities. It may mean practicing nonviolent communication as one grows in understanding of the workings of white supremacy and patriarchy in organizations one is a part of, or disentangling and resisting the greed and attachment that manifest in our economic systems and the natural world. Healing justice may mean practicing compassionate self-care in one's own life, seeking restoration and connection in a world caught in

a maelstrom of digital capitalism, speed, and overwork. For people whose bodies do not conform to the status quo or have been targeted with violence, compassionate self-care and 'radical self-love' become acts of resistance. As Audre Lorde famously said, 'caring for myself is not self-indulgence, it is self-preservation, and that is an act of political warfare.'

Healing justice can also look like coming together to sing, move, make music, tell stories, or to process grief.

I encourage you to do some of your own learning about these movements to help inform your journey. You might research the authors and teachers I mention in this section[47] or create/join a healing justice reading group. Perhaps there is a healing justice/disability justice collective or health justice organization in your community that you can support or participate in. I am including some healing justice principles in the following pages, which have been adopted and iterated on at healing justice gatherings in the last decade. I recommend looking up the lists I'm borrowing from and reading them in context.

One way you can practice healing justice as a spoonie is by being mindful of *how* you choose to do your healing, especially if you hold race and class privilege. I invite you to consider: Are you willing to be political in your healing? Are you willing to heal in community, in relationship with others?

If you have a choice, who are you choosing as your healers and how do they interact with the communities they are part of? What modalities are they practicing and how did they learn them? Are they running practices/businesses that you consider just and inclusive? Maybe take a moment here and reflect on these questions in your healing journal or come back to them at the end of this chapter. If you are in a position to pay for non-allopathic healing therapies, can you

---

47 Healing Justice Lineages: Dreaming at the Crossroads of Liberation, Collective Care, and Safety by Cara Page and Erica Woodland is an excellent primer on healing justice past, present, and future.

do so in a way that lifts up Black, brown, disabled, queer, Indigenous, and trans healers in your community?

Can you support practitioners or health organizations that also provide low-cost or no-cost healing to the community? When you decide to work with a healer, are you asking about the modalities they use, the lineages they come from, and discerning whether they are practicing cultural appropriation or cultural appreciation? These are some important questions to ask.

I encourage you to think about how you want to practice healing in responsible and ethical ways that center the most marginalized in our communities, instead of harming, excluding, or exploiting them. Supporting and uplifting marginalized healers is a really important part of building a truly inclusive system of care. It's part of restoring some of the healing traditions that were lost or nearly eradicated when white men took over healing professions in the West in the late 19th and early 20th century.

10 Principles of Disability Justice:

A complete list of the 10 Principles of Disability Justice by Sins Invalid and descriptions for each principle can be found online at tinyurl.com/DJ10Principles.

1. Intersectionality
2. Leadership of those most impacted
3. Anti-Capitalist Politics
4. Cross-movement solidarity
5. Recognizing wholeness
6. Sustainability
7. Commitment to cross-disability solidarity
8. Interdependence
9. Collective Access
10. Collective Liberation

Favorite Healing Justice Principles:
Here are some of my Healing Justice favorite principles. Complete lists are available online.

From the Healing & Health Justice Collective Organizing Principles, created at the US Social Forum in Detroit in 2010:[48]

- We are learning and creating this political framework about a legacy of healing and liberation that is meeting a particular moment in history inside of our movements that seeks to: regenerate traditions that have been lost; to mindfully hold contradictions in our practices; and to be conscious of the conditions we are living and working inside of as healers and organizers in our communities and movements.
- We believe in transparency on all levels so that we can have a foundation of trust, openness and honesty in our vision and action together.
- We believe in open source knowledge; which means that all information and knowledge is to be shared and transferred to create deeper collaboration and cross-movement building strategy.
- We believe that there is no such thing as joining this process too late; as we move forward, anyone who comes in when they come in are welcomed; and we will always remember that we are interconnected with many communities, struggles and legacies who have joined healing and resiliency practices with liberation in their work for centuries.

---

48 "Reflections from Detroit: Transforming Wellness & Wholeness," INCITE!, August 12, 2018, https://incite-national.org/2010/08/05/reflections-from-detroit-transforming-wellness-wholeness/.

From the 2012 Allied Media Conference Healing Justice Practice Space Principles:[49]

- We begin by listening.
- We honor individual and community agency, intuition, and innate wisdom, and therefore honor people's rights to make decisions about their own bodies.
- We understand that health and wellness should be determined by the individual or community receiving care, and for many of us this includes the reality of disability, illness, and harm reduction. We accept and encourage individuals and communities defining health, healing, and wellness for themselves, and not based on normative models of healing.
- We center the genius and leadership of disabled and chronically ill communities, for what we know about surviving and resisting the medical industrial complex and living with fierce beauty in our sick and disabled bodies. We say no to the medical industrial complex's model of "cure or be useless," instead working from a place of belief in the wholeness of disability, interdependence and disabled people as inherently good as we are.

From Badass Visionary Healers' Healing Justice Principles:[50]
Some things we believe in:

- Resisting the "cure" model and understanding that for many people, the goal of healing is not a "perfect" able body.
- Challenging fatphobia, using a Health at Every Size framework and creating healing spaces for all bodies to define what healthy means for them.
- Building and maintaining relationship to the land as part of our healing practices.

49 https://justhealing.files.wordpress.com/2012/04/hjps-guidingprinciples.pdf As shared in "Healing Justice Practice Spaces: A How To Guide," released December 18, 2014.

50 "Healing Justice Principles: Some of What We Believe," Bad Ass Visionary Healers, October 20, 2012, https://badassvisionaryhealers.wordpress.com/healing-justice-principles/.

From Black Lives Matter's 10 Reasons Why Healing Justice:[51]

1. Trauma, violence, and oppression live on and through our bodies limiting our experience, our connection and choice.

2. Freedom for Black people must include healing that address the individual and collective, the current and the generational pain

3. Our healing brings us into new kinds of relationships with one another

4. Healing justice and transformative justice remind us that conflict can be generative and a way to care for each other and learn more about our needs and boundaries

5. Healing allows us to move away from scarcity and fear and into connection and choice

6. The trauma Black people feel is compounded, often constant and complex. Building a world that creates space and time for Black people to heal and limits the trauma they experience requires a deep reworking and reimagining of relationships and institutions

7. Healing, culture and spirit have always sustained us and informed our struggles for liberation

8. Healing justice allows us a place to practice the care with each other that we each deserve

9. Healing justice makes care political in a world that harms and dehumanizes Black bodies

10. Healing justice makes it possible to transform and heal a legacy of trauma for future generations of Black people

Reflection Questions:
- How do you feel after reading the principles above?
- Do you see opportunities to bring some of the principles of healing justice and disability justice into your paid or passion work, your community, or your personal healing?

---

51 "Resources," Black Lives Matter, accessed July 17, 2019, https://blacklivesmatter.com/resources/.

SECTION 3

HOW TO HEAL

At this point you have some basic healing tools, and a lot of fodder to answer the question, "Why heal?" We've also looked at the connection between personal healing and collective healing and how choosing to heal can contribute to our collective wellbeing and liberation. Hopefully you are closer to believing that focusing on your healing is the best thing you can do for yourself, your community, and the world. This section will give you principles and more concrete tools to support your journey on the healing path.

In this section, we'll look more closely at *how* to heal, personally and collectively. What follows is not a prescription, but a collection of suggestions and guideposts to support you on the healing path. First, I offer principles that I've developed from my own time on the healing path and years of working with clients. They provide anchors for your energy and attention, to serve as a reminder of what healing is actually all about (rather than what society tells us it is). I recommend spending a little time exploring each principle, inside and outside of reading this book, to see where there are possibilities and openings for you. The rest of the section explores different approaches to the mental, emotional, and spiritual aspects of healing according to the principles. It's a high-level survey and by no means an exhaustive list. My goal was to share some highlights of what's out there and spark further internal and external exploration.

I focus on the mental, emotional, and spiritual aspects of healing pain and illness because I have found they are vital, but too often overlooked. There are a lot of amazing books, practitioners, and modalities out there that focus on healing the body with physical healing modalities, including detoxing, diet, exercise, acupuncture, bodywork and countless others.

There is also a lot of cool work happening on body-based approaches to healing trauma, such as Somatic Experiencing, which aims to release trauma held as tension in the physical body to heal Post Traumatic Stress Disorder and other mental health challenges. Because trauma and physical illness are so linked, trauma-releasing modalities can help with physical health conditions too, and I recommend everyone pursue some kind of somatic healing for emotional wellness at some point in their journey.

But even as awareness of the impact of trauma on chronic health conditions grows, there isn't enough public dialogue about the psycho-spiritual-emotional aspects of physical illness, and how vital it is to address those aspects in concert with body-based healing modalities. Cultural conversation about this *is* growing: the 2017 Netflix documentary "Heal" raised awareness about the importance of these aspects of healing, Dr. Gabor Maté and others speak about the trauma-illness connection, and there have been a lot of studies on the mind-body connection—but still—most folks don't get any guidance on this part of healing in the doctor's office.

One of my goals is to support your mind to become an ally in your healing, instead of a foe. Our inner critic can keep us from doing what we know we need to do to heal, sometimes for years at a time. So, it's a lot easier to find success with body-based healing modalities when it's done in tandem with some kind of brain training.

Brain training could look like meditation, ontological coaching, positive visualization, or other ways of interrupting our inner critic's unhelpful thought patterns. There is a lot of evidence supporting this but one of my favorite examples is Dr. John Sarno, a rehab doctor, who helped patients eliminate extremely debilitating chronic back pain in a matter of days simply by teaching them how to observe and manage their thought patterns.[52]

Like your brain, if your spirit or soul isn't on board to heal, healing isn't going to happen. I see this a lot in my coaching work. Someone will be mentally and emotionally ready to make changes in their life but spiritually they feel skeptical, depleted, or scared. The root of this is nearly always disconnection. We need to feel at least a little held by others in order to heal.

Sometimes it's just being held by the earth, or animals, because we don't feel like we can trust people or the divine, and that's okay, but since most of us are disconnected from ourselves, we need to feel at least one point of connection to move through the transformation required for healing. As we've explored throughout this book, healing is not a solo affair. Ideally, we feel and work with multiple points of connection as we move along the healing path. I'll say more about all of this in the Disconnect and Reconnect chapter.

As you read this third and final section, I invite you to try what resonates and not worry about the rest. There are no rules, and you get to be the author of your own healing journey. As in the previous

---

52 "SimplySarno," accessed February 8, 2023, https://simplysarno.com/.

section, every chapter here contains exercises or reflection questions. If you're exhausted, or impatient like me, it might be tempting to blow them off—but I really recommend taking the time to consider the questions and try the exercises.

At the very least, if it's accessible to you, jot down a few notes in your healing journal after each chapter about what gets you excited, what you're learning, and what feels worth learning more about vs. what doesn't resonate at this time. If any of the principles feel especially resonant with you, you might write them down and put them up somewhere in your space so you can metaphorically chew on them further and see what they have to teach you.

As you're reading or listening, I also recommend recording whatever is working well and shifting, no matter how small. This will give your brain evidence that you are in fact moving forward, even when your inner critic has a lot to say about how far you still have to go, or how hopeless the whole pursuit of healing is.

Maybe you can't play basketball, but you're being a lot kinder to yourself, and that's freaking huge. That self-compassion is going to help you in all kinds of ways. It may support you in getting back to playing basketball, and faster than you would otherwise. After this section, I'll offer additional resources and ways to get in touch with me if you'd like to work together on your healing.

Rebel Healing Principles

"In today's America, we tend to think of healing as a binary: either we're broken or we're healed from that brokenness. But that's not how healing operates, and it's almost never how human growth works. More often, healing and growth take place on a continuum, with innumerable points between utter brokenness and total health."

—Resmaa Menakem

Principle - noun - *A fundamental truth or proposition that serves as the foundation for a system of belief or behavior or for a chain of reasoning.*

Healing is typically not easy, not linear, and totally unpredictable. Our experience of it is largely influenced by how we choose to be with the changes our bodies force or invite us to make. Here I think it will be helpful to explore and define what healing really is so we can pursue it with more clarity and ease. As a reminder, I am speaking primarily about non-physical healing, but this exploration can apply to physical healing too.

At the most basic level, healing requires you to say "yes" to all that is. This is usually challenging in practice because of all the crap we have to overcome in the process. There might be a lot of gunk in the way, namely social programming and past trauma that is living in your body that you may not even be aware of. In my own life, there have been things that feel impossibly hard to do and I don't have words to explain why. I chalk that up to unmetabolized pain, and I've had to keep coming back to the hard things to let them unfold and unravel over time. Only then have I gained some understanding of what was going on. It is normal that the internal and external barriers to saying "yes" to all of yourself can feel totally insurmountable. But that doesn't mean they actually are.

In this chapter I have outlined some principles to support you on your journey to saying "yes" to all of yourself. They have been informed by my personal experience and what has worked for my clients and people in my community. I like principles because they can make a complex process or approach easier to wrap your head around.

Also, let's be real: A lot of folks reading or listening to this book are going to have brain fog and I figure, even if you forget everything else, or don't get through the rest of this book, you can at least write these principles on a sticky note, or record yourself saying them into a voice memo, and try them on as wayfinders for your healing journey. I personally struggled with reading for years, so if you're like me, and you only read this chapter—great job! You get a sticker! Make that sticky note and pass this book on to someone else.

I'll explain what all the principles mean in more detail in the coming pages. What I want to give you most is a set of tools to help you feel more in touch with who you really are, and feel more at home in your body. Seeing who you really are can be wicked uncomfortable. And accepting it, especially if your friends, coworkers, or family of origin disapprove, is a whole different layer. Feeling at home in your body, even if it's not in pain, can be difficult simply because our society is very brain-forward and our bodies don't get the attention they deserve. And the challenge of fully inhabiting one's body is exacerbated by trauma.

But learning how to be, just be, with your body and all of yourself is totally possible. These principles are designed to support you in shifting your mindset and your behavior so that you can see and accept your beautiful self with love, and experience more ease, aliveness, and connection in your everyday life, no matter what's happening in your body. The principles are also meant to be empowering and remind you that you have agency in your healing.

In the following sections I will share recommendations for lifestyle shifts, practices, and healing modalities that might support you in adopting and living from the principles. Everything is just a suggestion. If you try something and it doesn't work for you, that's okay.

Don't beat yourself up if what worked for me and your friend Josephine doesn't work for you. It might be that there are internal or environmental factors working against you that are currently beyond your awareness or control. Resist the urge to blame yourself for any perceived failure or lack of progress. If something doesn't work for you, it might be that it's not the right fit for you, or not the right time, and coming back to it later could yield a different experience.

As I've said before, the important thing to remember is that there's no right way or one way to heal. There's only *your* way, and the more you practice training the mind, healing trauma, cultivating your spiritual connection, loving yourself, and healing in community with others, the easier it will be for you to see your unique next steps.

Principles of Rebel Healing:
1. Healing is Change
2. Healing is Feeling
3. Healing is Embodiment
4. Healing is Loving All of Yourself
5. Healing is Training Your Brain (To Be Your Ally)
6. Healing is Listening and Honoring Your Truth
7. Healing Happens in Community
8. Healing Makes Liberation Possible

Healing is Change

Suit up and get ready to see that everything you know about yourself and the world may need to change in order for you to grow into your most full, authentic, and vital self. Healing doesn't look like getting back to the way things were before—the way things were before made you sick. Healing is seeing clearly what does not serve you, and being willing to switch up anything that is in your control.

The flip side of this is accepting what's not in your control. That urge to try to get better, to fix things immediately, is a natural reaction to becoming ill or experiencing pain. We're always trying to minimize our discomfort and find solutions quickly. One of my teachers, Alex Amorosi, reminded me of the extremely powerful saying, "Everything in its own time." It's a nice way of saying "You have no control so stop trying so hard and slow the F down already!" Not everything needs to happen right now.

You may not want to hear that, but urgency may have been part of what landed you here in the first place—your own hurry to do things and/or our societal emphasis on needing everything done ASAP, which is a central tenet of white supremacy culture.[53] The reality is that there is no quick fix in healing, so there's no need to look for one.

Noticing your reaction to the healing timeline is an opportunity to observe how internalized kyriarchal social constructs may have trained you to celebrate the quick fix and perhaps overlook the less glamorous stories of change and hard work overtime.

You will heal. It's going to happen, and one of the best things you can do is stop trying to drive the bus every moment and give the process some space. We often get overwhelmed with all the possible next steps we could take. To center yourself, continuously come back to your vision for healing and wholeness and take the next best step to live from your vision. As my teacher Dr. Maria Nemeth says, we experience ease when we learn "simply to do what is next on our path, moment by moment."[54]

Trust that your body is always trying to heal itself on its own timeline, just as plants are always trying to grow. Everything in nature

---

53 I talked about white supremacy culture in Section 2, but to explore this more in depth, check out https://www.whitesupremacyculture.info/

54 Dr. Maria Nemeth, "Being a Conscious Conduit of Energy" (Academy for Coaching Excellence, 2005).

and in our biology is constantly and collectively supporting life. Life, life, and more life. When you're experiencing dis-ease, there's simply something in the way, keeping your body from healing itself, like a tree shading another plant from the sun. The blockage could be something physical, like a blocked artery, or energetic, like trauma or emotional funk. It's usually both.

Your job is to listen for instructions—from your body and your intuition—so that you can clear whatever is blocking the healing and seek out the right support to do so. There are millions of healers and modalities out there, and if you listen, your body will tell you what kind of help you need, and maybe even who to see, where to find them, and how to pay for/trade for the healing or get support for free.

Seeking the support your body needs will require you to change. You will need to stand up for yourself, say "no" to people you love, and honor your unique gifts. This might involve being willing to pursue a life path that is unconventional and/or do other things that are outside your current comfort zone. Avoiding discomfort is one of the biggest barriers to a successful healing journey. So, if you're not already there, it would behoove you to pursue a friendship with discomfort, even if it's, well, uncomfortable. We'll talk more about befriending discomfort in Cultivate Self-Love, later in this section.

Embracing change and discomfort to heal is also necessary on a collective level. Healing takes time. Social change takes time. Both take rigor, perseverance, and a lot of faith. African Americans and allies organized for 99 years between the original Juneteenth[55] in 1865 and the passing of the Civil Rights Act in 1964 and have continued through present day. Rosa Parks organized for 11 years before she sat in the front of that bus, the singular act that brought her notoriety. We all have a stake in uprooting the oppressive systems that are blocking

---

55 "Juneteenth commemorates the June 19, 1865, announcement of the abolition of slavery in Texas, and more generally the emancipation of enslaved African Americans throughout the former Confederate States of America, outside Native American lands." "Juneteenth," Wikipedia (Wikimedia Foundation, January 18, 2023), https://en.wikipedia.org/wiki/Juneteenth.

many people from healing and pursuing their dreams—for example, a Black person whose vision for healing is consistently undercut by white supremacy culture and institutional racism.

Our systems rob communities of dreams, resources, health, and lives every day. This is why the connection between personal and collective healing is so important. We cannot heal fully unless everyone is healing fully, and that requires us to dismantle white supremacy, racial capitalism, and ableism, and create new systems that support collective joy and well-being. Healing requires us to change the way we move through the world and do our part to upend the social systems that are keeping us all unwell.

Healing is Feeling

Healing involves allowing yourself to feel all that we've been trained out of feeling. Modern life in America, with its multi-layered oppression, desensitizes us to human suffering and joy, and everything in between. Dominant culture values the mind over both feelings and sensations in the body. We are taught to ignore that information in favor of rationality and critical thinking. This culture, rooted in colonialism, patriarchy, and white supremacy, demonizes feelings and teaches us that showing them is weak and unbecoming, something to be avoided and apologized for when it happens.

We all know how this is working for us. It's not. It's part of how we ended up here, with systems that harm instead of supporting life. Personal and societal transformation ask us to open our hearts and relearn what it means to feel. Collective empathy starts at the personal level. We must be willing and able to feel our feelings and sensations in order to fully empathize with others.

Healing is Embodiment

Trauma educator and somatic guide Kimberly Ann Johnson, writes in her book, *Call of the Wild: How We Heal Our Trauma, Awaken Our Own Power, and Use it For Good* that, "Embodiment —or being anchored and aware within your body—requires learning to perceive what is already there without manipulating it. Your body tells its own story and is capable of healing."[56]

Learning to listen to, honor, and inhabit your body is one of the most important parts of healing. Modern colonized society is very mind-centric, so many of us lose our connection to our bodies as we become educated and socialized. But you can regain this connection to your body. In fact, one of the most courageous and effective things you can pursue in your healing journey is presence.

Buddhism teaches that there is no separation between mind and body. There is only the present moment. When you can acknowledge your discomfort and be present anyway, life gets a lot easier. The suffering we experience doesn't come from the pain or illness we have—it comes from the story we tell about it, and the meaning we assign to it. Life is uncomfortable, whether you experience physical discomfort or not. Avoiding discomfort is avoiding the inevitable. You're going to feel pain in one way or another. It's best to start making friends with it now.

Pain is simply a signal that things are out of order. It's normal for things to be out of order sometimes, and it's good to know when things are out of order so we can attempt to support our body in healing. If it hurts to bend our leg a certain way, it's worth paying attention to that so we don't end up with a strained ligament for example. The signal is worth acknowledging, and something we can choose to be grateful for. When I remember, I'll even say to my body, "Thank you.

---

56 Kimberly Ann Johnson, The Call of the Wild: How We Heal Trauma, Awaken Our Own Power, and Use It for Good (New York, NY: Harper Wave, 2021).

I appreciate this message," and that can be enough to ease the pain a little. I share other practices for embracing discomfort in the Train Your Brain section.

When I experience pain or a new symptom, I try first to practice being grateful for the information, and then practice being curious, "Huh. Isn't it interesting that I am having asthma for the first time in 12 years? I wonder what that's about." Notice that I said "practice" being grateful and then curious. Even the most practiced healers will forget this in a crisis so don't beat yourself up when you get a new symptom and freak out about it. That's normal. Just try this curiosity thing on and over time it might support you in changing your relationship to your symptoms.

Sometimes our brains or bodies get off track and set off warning signs erroneously or unnecessarily, as in autoimmune diseases, and it can be harder to have gratitude for that. But, like a neurodivergent or disabled child, can you learn to love it and see its perfection even though it doesn't work the "normal" way? Even a misfiring brain or body deserves our love and compassion.

Healing is a practice of coming back to our biological and primal instincts, tuning in to the nervous system, and receiving the instructions we are given by the body. The more we do this, the more energy and internal resources we can cultivate. The body knows how to heal and will tell us what it needs. We just have to listen.

Healing is Loving All of Yourself

My mentor Beth Ann Suggs, who is a minister, trainer of coaches, and incredibly wise woman, says that healing is an exercise in being with our wholeness—the good and the bad, the shiny and the broken parts. Your wholeness includes your body, your soul, your brain, your likes and dislikes, the traumas you carry in your body and psyche, and the ways that you respond to stress, conflict, and joy. To heal is to learn to love and accept all of yourself, whether your pain and illness can go away or not. The promise of loving and accepting your wholeness will help you live with more ease, joy, presence, gratitude, and a greater capacity to contribute. And being able to contribute to others is what we all want at our core. It cultivates connection and adds great sweetness and meaning to our lives.

Depending on the cards we were dealt when we came into the world, all of us have at least nicks, if not gaping holes, in our wholeness. Just being a human being is traumatic, and living in a society that values some lives over others, and values profit over life, adds a whole additional layer of trauma for your cells to handle. By learning to love your messy, beautiful, complex, and complicated wholeness, you can experience life in an entirely new way, with a greater sense of abundance and possibility—even in a toxic context.

Even if you don't know how yet, see if you might be willing to love yourself with the ferocity of a momma bear. Ideally, you treat yourself with the patience you would show a four-year-old and the reverence you might show an ancient grandmother. Ideally, you treat yourself as you would your favorite person in the whole world, with a whole lotta love.

Having your own back like this may involve learning to lovingly say "no" to others when needed so that you can more easily say "yes" to yourself. The more you love yourself and honor the needs of your body and soul, the easier it is to maintain clear boundaries and advocate for yourself and your needs. Nobody changes the world, heals from health challenges, or achieves personal transformation by being a people pleaser.

Healing is Training Your Brain (To Be Your Ally)

Healing requires getting your whole being on board the healing train. The brain—which we still don't know all that much about —isn't always a team player in the healing process, despite good intentions. It will think it's helping tremendously, helping you weigh pros and cons of something, or getting into problem-solving mode, but the natural worrying that it does, and its desire to have an answer for everything, can actually keep your nervous system from calming down enough to heal.

Writer, pleasure activist, and Black liberation facilitator adrienne maree brown has spread the idea that "what you pay attention to grows." She explains: "attention is one of our most valuable resources. in your own life, attention is what determines the quality of your lived experience. if your attention stays on what's wrong, on your powerlessness and pain, you can become identified with a victimized, power under narrative, and that will grow. if your attention is instead on gratitude, collective power, experimentation, curiosity and celebration, these things will grow in your life. brené brown and oprah and ava and all the manifestors know this."[57]

This practice of "attention liberation" is an essential skill to develop on the healing path. Applied to our context, when you give your pain and illness a lot of your attention, it will take that attention and run with it. When you focus on what's hurting or not working, that heightens the experience and keeps the nervous system dysregulated. But we actually have the option to choose where we put our attention. And, as brown also shares, when we practice liberating our attention, we can experience more focus, make healthier life choices, and better feel our own agency.

You can train your brain to direct your attention in service of your healing, instead of against it. There are multiple ways to do this, including practicing mindfulness, using affirmations, or completing brain rewiring programs like the Dynamic Neural Retraining System. I will share more about this in the Train Your Brain chapter, but to start

57 "Attention Liberation, attention reparations" adrienne maree brown, October 18, 2017, http://adriennemaree-brown.net/2017/10/28/attention-liberation-attention-reparations/.

off, I want to invite you to start noticing when your brain is going into panic mode. Common triggers include new symptoms of any kind, a sudden onset of pain, significant life events, or any change in your treatment protocol. Practice telling your brain, "I hear you, and we don't need to figure this out right this moment." Then you can follow that with some deep breaths, meditation, yoga, or whatever practice helps you calm your nervous system.

Healing is Listening and Honoring Your Truth

French mime and teacher of movement and physical theater Jacques Lecoq is quoted as saying, "The body knows things about which the mind is ignorant." This is just the truth. For all the value we put on critical thinking and the cognitive mind, we only use it in 2-5% of our total time on Earth. The other 95-98% of the time we operate from more instinctual knowledge.

When our thinking mind doesn't know what to do, the feeling, sensing mind does. Learning to tap into that wisdom regularly and honor the information you receive, even if your mind isn't sure, is the key to answering most of life's biggest questions, including how to heal. Your body already knows how to heal. It's literally designed to do it. The body also has a huge database to pull from—all your lived experience, the experience of your ancestors, and learnings from the entire human race.

Those little intuitive hits you get, the gut feelings, good and bad vibes, those feelings that come out of nowhere? That's where the magic is. Ask your body questions and practice listening. If something hurts, or doesn't sit right in your gut, don't do it just because someone is telling you to—even if they are known to be the best, most talented, most sparkly whatever they are. Acting in ways that are not aligned with your values and intuition will stunt your healing and could cause a lot of suffering. Your body will also tell you who to date and not date, what to do to earn income, where to live, and what gifts are yours to share with the world. Practice asking, listening, and acting accordingly.

Healing Happens in Community

This principle's essence comes from from Aurora Levins Morales, who wrote in her book *Medicine Stories*, "Healing takes place in community, in the telling and bearing of witness, in the naming of trauma and in the grief and rage and defiance that follow."[58] Part of the reason so many folks are sick in this country is precisely because we are disconnected from each other and ourselves. The only way we can heal fully is in community with others.

We need to see that our suffering is everyone's suffering and our triumph is everyone's triumph. Dori Midnight, a social justice witch based in Western Massachusetts, said it another way, that "healing is connection."[59] Connecting, sharing our stories, allowing ourselves to be seen in our pain, and supporting each other allows us to grow as individuals and supports the health of our community.

When we see our suffering in the context of collective suffering, we experience freedom from the gripping nature of our own pain. It also creates opportunity for collaborative healing, which is both more fun and more effective than trying to heal in isolation. Deep connection is part of the foundation for collective liberation, so healing in community provides an important prerequisite for effective social change. And connection means more than connecting with other humans. I invite you to consider the animals, plants, and spirit(s) around you as part of your community too and entities deserving of connection and attention.

Healing is also just easier when we get help from others. Some of us get all torn up about asking for help, worrying that we might be

---

58 Levins Aurora Morales, Medicine Stories: Essays for Radicals (Durham: Duke University Press, 2019).

59 "Dori Midnight," Dori Midnight, accessed February 2, 2023, https://dorimidnight.com/.

a burden, or that we won't be able to return the favor. Support isn't a quid pro quo situation. It's part of being in the human family. Some people need more support than others and some people are happy to offer more support than others. It all evens out in the wash. We all need support to survive and thrive, and we also need to contribute to feel connected. And you, you gorgeous healer, may need more support now so you can support others more later. I invite you to be willing to ask for and receive a little (or a lot of) extra support when you need it. Some people will say "no," and that's okay. Others will say "yes," and feel grateful that you asked.

When we create mutual systems of support, it can bring ease to our own healing and bolster the healing of others. No matter how compromised or disabled, most of us can find ways to both give and receive. I've seen bed-bound folks with ME/CFS and Lyme contribute to our collective liberation in huge ways, from writing legislation to hearing and validating the experience of other patients in Facebook groups. It's also just important to have buddies who get it, who you can laugh, cry, and celebrate with you on your journey. My Lyme buddies are some of the greatest treasures in my life. I strongly suggest you seek out at least one spoonie healing buddy if you don't already have that kind of relationship with someone. This is because spoonies can see you and affirm your choices in a way that most able-bodied people cannot.

Disclaimer: Not all communities are healing. For example, social justice organizations and healing support groups can be nourishing and/or traumatizing depending on the culture of the group and who is facilitating it. As I discuss in Section 3, Build Your Support Dream Team, if you're in the process of calling in a healing community, I recommend allowing yourself to dream up your ideal community and write it down or create a vision board so you can recognize your people when you see them.

Healing Makes Liberation Possible

As I discussed in Section 2, doing the mental, emotional, and spiritual work required to heal health challenges is a contribution to our collective liberation in many ways. And the contributions come as much from what you do as what you stop doing in the process of healing.

Sick people are traumatized people. Traumatized people, if they do not or cannot metabolize (heal) their trauma, end up perpetuating it in their relationships—with their families, coworkers, neighbors, and whoever else they might encounter. This looks like abuse, neglect, addiction, racism, homophobia, and other forms of physical and emotional violence.

Trauma shows up at the familial and societal level. If you went to school, think about all the teachers you ever had and how they might have unknowingly passed some of their trauma on to you and other students in how they spoke, how they taught, how they treated students with different identities, and how they dealt with challenging situations in the classroom. And how might that have impacted you? How might it have impacted your classmates?

Choosing to heal, and healing the trauma that lives in you enables you to do less harm—to your familial line, our human community, the earth, and the people you interact with every day.

As you do your healing work, if you don't already, you will see that everyone has trauma to heal. Since trauma can be a physical manifestation of oppression, the more you understand about your own trauma, the easier it is to see that everyone is harmed by oppressive systems, and some much more than others. With that lens, you naturally become more compassionate and collectively attuned in your words and actions.

If you are not on the healing path, you may be projecting your suffering and discomfort on everyone else and wondering why life feels so hard. But, when you commit to the healing path, and you have little breakthroughs along the way, it frees up your energy to be more present with yourself and those around you. In today's world, presence is precious. Being able to leave your struggles at the door and show up for someone else is a real gift. Or being able and willing to be in the struggle *with* others in their struggle is equally valuable. The more we can do that for each other, the more easily we can all heal, and feel supported and emboldened to invest energy in creating the future we dream of—like one with a healthcare system that facilitates real, holistic healing without causing so much harm.

Disconnect and Reconnect

"I can gather all the news I need on the weather report."
—Simon & Garfunkel

*"We might think that the confusion we experience in our daily
life happens in isolation, but in reality it has something to do
with our lack of connection to our ancestors."*
—Sobonfu Somé

This chapter is about the importance of *disconnecting* from things
that don't serve you so that you can *reconnect* with yourself and other
beings. We are going to look at disconnecting from smart phones,
media, and social media, since they are some of the most omnipresent
and seductive attention suckers at this time in our history. I'll offer a
few different ways to turn down the noise in your life and come back
to yourself.

Think of these as suggestions to help you start noticing where
your attention might be getting hijacked so that you can redirect it to
healing, joy, and connection. Recentering in yourself can allow you to
regain energy and attention and show up for others with more presence, all of which creates more possibility for grounded and effective
social change. I'll also discuss different points of connection that you
can explore, including connecting with your body, the Earth, your
ancestors, and the divine.[60]

If the word "divine" scares you, I promise I won't proselytize about
any particular way of being with it. I am simply offering another way

---

60 A couple years after writing this section I learned about the work of Dare Sohei who refers to these connections
as the Four Pillars of Attachment. To hear more about Dare's framework, I recommend Episode 2 of The Ritual As
Justice Podcast, "E02: Attachment and Allyship," posted July 7, 2020.

to track where you're putting your attention so you can, if you want to, make changes and align your attention to things that actually serve you. You can think of these different points of connection as relationships that can anchor and guide you on the healing path, especially when things feel tumultuous or unclear.

If you haven't already, I highly recommend taking a step back from screens, the constant hum of the 24-hour news cycle, and social media in the interest of giving your brain and your nervous system a rest. When your attention is wrapped up in the matters of others, whether it's people in your community, folks you follow on Instagram, or the latest public tragedy, you aren't spending the time you need to spend with yourself to hear what your body and soul need to heal.

Of course, you'll want to be present to other folks sometimes, and if you're a parent or caregiver, you just have to. It's also arguably good to know what's going on in the world. But it's also good to notice if you use the news, social media, other people's drama, your kids, or even activism as a distraction from looking and seeing what's really going on for you. Big problems and other people's stuff can be really juicy, seductive, and addictive.

Keeping your attention externally focused like that is also easy to justify: "Well I *need* to know what's going on to be a good citizen," or "Jessie is in a bad way and really needs someone to talk to about what's going on for her." Yes, *and* it's always good to check-in with yourself and see if perhaps you're giving these things more energy or attention than you have or want to give, or significantly more energy and attention than you're giving yourself. Here we'll look at how to notice if that's happening, and how to transform that pattern in service of your healing.

Let's start with phones. It's pretty clear at this point that smartphones, while amazing tools of connection, also possess the capacity to disrupt our lives, namely by messing with our sleep[61] and increasing levels of anxiety[62] and depression.[63] If you have your phone in your room when you're sleeping, even if it's off, part of your brain is waiting all night in anticipation of what will appear on the screen in the morning. Eek!

Unless you're already good at using screens sparingly, you're likely going to want to find a way to keep your phone outside your bedroom when you sleep and limit the time you spend on your phone. Checking your phone a lot, or even just having it around, keeps part of your brain distracted.[64] If your phone is around while you're doing other things, that divides your brain's attention, which drains your energy.

If you find yourself checking your phone more than twice an hour without being required to do so for your job, it might be time to see if you can shift your relationship. There are lots of great guides online with hacks to decrease phone time, and a few of my clients really enjoyed Catherine Price's book, *How to Break Up with Your Phone.* I recommend using an app like Moment, or the system built into your phone, to track your screen time and build awareness.

I have my phone set up to be black and white so it appears less sexy and seductive to my brain. I also leave my phone outside my room at night and use an alarm clock. Still, maintaining boundaries with my phone is a struggle sometimes, especially when I am waiting to hear from people I love. Be kind and patient with yourself. Phones are designed to be addictive, and changing habits takes time.

Then there's news and TV. I started watching the evening news with my dad at two years old. It was how I spent time with him when

61 Scutti, Susan. "Your Smartphone May Be Hurting Your Sleep." CNN. Cable News Network, June 23, 2017. https://www.cnn.com/2016/11/09/health/smartphones-harm-sleep/index.html.

62 "Warning: Reading This on a Smartphone May Cause Anxiety, Researchers Say," Los Angeles Times, June 7, 2019, https://www.latimes.com/nation/la-na-smartphones-causing-student-anxiety-20190607-story.html.

63 "Which Comes First: Smartphone Dependency or Depression?" ScienceDaily, accessed May 4, 2020, https://www.sciencedaily.com/releases/2019/09/190930161918.htm.

64 Adrian F. Ward et al., "Brain Drain: The Mere Presence of One's Own Smartphone Reduces Available Cognitive Capacity," Journal of the Association for Consumer Research 2, no. 2 (May 1, 2017): pp. 140-154, https://doi.org/10.1086/691462.

he came home from work. I grew up thinking of the late ABC news anchor Peter Jennings as my second father and I cried hard when he passed. I also thought I wanted to be a journalist for a long time because journalists were my heroes. So, it wasn't easy for me to change my news consumption habits. It felt like a part of me, and one I didn't want to give up.

I decided to make the change when I read Katina Makris' beautiful memoir about her Lyme healing journey, *Out of the Woods: Healing Lyme Disease and Other Chronic Illness – Body, Mind, & Spirit.*[65] She shares in the book that one of her practitioners told her not to watch or consume anything adrenaline-producing. No action movies. No TV news. (This was a few years before I found the Dynamic Neural Retraining System, which suggests the same—essentially to keep your brain in a calm, happy place while you rewire the limbic system. It makes sense!) I liked the sound of this practice and decided to give it a try.

For about three years, I only watched and read comedy, and I limited my daily news intake to the National Public Radio (NPR) Newscast, which is less than five minutes. This restriction was especially helpful during the 2016 election cycle! I still love keeping up with the news, and my idea of a great weeknight is getting to eat dinner, pet a dog, and watch or listen to the PBS NewsHour. Still, having more discretion around when and how I consume news has helped me protect my mental and emotional landscape, which in turn supports my physical wellbeing.

How much you restrict or allow yourself to consume media is going to depend on your current habits and how sensitive you are. If you're already totally or mostly unplugged and you feel good about it, you can skip down to "Connect with Yourself." If you're news-obsessed, a big TV watcher, or you spend a lot of time on social media,

---

65 Katina I. Makris, Out of the Woods: Healing Lyme Disease and Other Chronic Illness – Body, Mind, & Spirit (New York, NY: Skyhorse Publishing, 2015).

I encourage you to take stock of how much potentially triggering/ nervous-system-activating media you consume. Experiment with curtailing your intake, or perhaps start a full out media fast, totally cutting yourself off for a while.

Here are some signs that it might be time to limit or bring some discipline to your phone time and/or (social) media consumption:
- You regularly pick up your phone to check it, even if there aren't any notifications
- You listen to NPR all day, or for as much of the day as you can
- You have a habit of watching 1-3 hours of news a night, and perhaps find yourself yelling at the screen
- You listen to podcasts all day (Even if it's all happy stuff)
- You don't go to sleep until way after your desired bedtime because you get sucked into Facebook, TikTok, Instagram, Reddit, YouTube or some other internet hole

All these activities can limit your healing by keeping your nervous system dysregulated (revisit Section 1, Step 1 for a refresher on this). As I've said before, healing requires a certain amount of spaciousness. You'll need more quiet time than other people, more time to just be so that your brain and nervous system can reset and heal.

Here are some simple ways to reduce your distracted time and carve out space to just be:
- If you're dining with others, focus on eating and talking to them. If you're dining alone, don't read or watch anything on a screen. If you want some stimulation, and it's accessible to you, try listening to something fun or soothing.
- Don't take your phone into the bathroom.

- If it's accessible to you, trade watching for reading whenever possible. I understand that some folks just can't read given the state of their health (I couldn't read for years) but if you can, try reading or listening to an audiobook or podcast instead of watching videos, movies, or TV. It works best if you do this with a book or media you're really excited about rather than something you feel you "should" read. If you've been reading back-to-back books on healing, try swapping in a novel, poetry, or a short story.
- Keep your phone outside your bedroom. You can get an alarm clock if you need one. For optimum sleep hygiene, it's recommended that you keep ALL electronics outside your bedroom and put your Wi-Fi on a timer so it turns off at night.
- If it's possible for you, see how many activities you can do without your phone. I like to go on walks and leave my phone at home, for example.

Once you're in a practice of disconnecting from media and social media, you'll start seeing more ways to reconnect. You'll be more present to yourself, your body's signals, the other people in your life, and the world around you. Next, I offer some possible points of connection to play with.

Connect with Yourself

Being connected with yourself means having some understanding of what's going on in your interior world: your body, your mind, your mood and emotional landscape. It involves checking in regularly with your body and emotional body, and noticing what you're experiencing, ideally without judgment.

Like most things, it gets easier and more useful the more you practice. I have personally found it easier to practice this alone and with regular time dedicated to it. But, tuning in to yourself is something you can practice on the fly, throughout the day, and while in relationship with others. No matter how you do it, the more you make space to practice noticing what's up inside, the better you get to know yourself and what you need, and the easier it becomes to check-in with yourself even in times of great chaos.

While it can sound trite, the first step is simply to make time for yourself. Creating even small pockets of solo time can be very nourishing for your healing journey. My healing journey actually turned me into more of an introvert, and I'm not upset about it! I understand that some folks work three jobs or are primary caregivers without a lot of support and might laugh at the notion of solo time. I see you! But, whatever your situation, it's worth trying to figure out how to carve out time, even if it's 10-20 minutes a day, or an extra two minutes in the bathroom.

If solo time is hard to come by, be on the lookout for opportunities to enroll support so that you make some space. Can you co-parent with a friend, or get a neighbor to watch your family member for 30 minutes so you can go for a walk? More time is better if you can swing it, and I would argue that the more stressed you feel, the more self-connection time you should take.

Start by doing what you can. If you're already alone a lot, which is true for a lot of spoonies, your work is to carve out some intentionally *undistracted* time. It's easy to spend lots of time alone without being intentional about using it to connect with yourself. Sometimes it helps to put yourself in a place or position that is out of the ordinary, outside your routine, which could be as simple as lying on the floor vs. a bed or couch. Sometimes that's enough to change your perspective.

When you set out to connect with yourself, put away books, devices, and other distractions so you can really be with you. Depending on what's accessible to you, you might spend your time meditating, going for a walk, making art, taking a bath, walking, sitting on a rock, or curled up in a blanket and staring out the window.

My favorite self-connection activities are taking baths, lying on the floor or in the grass, and sitting or lying by a body of water. You might keep your healing journal close by in case things come up that you want to record. You can also close your eyes, put your hand on your heart and ask yourself, "How am I feeling?" or "How are you feeling?" and notice what comes up.

After years of practicing self-connection, sometimes asking this of my heart is enough to elicit a big, cleansing ugly cry. Other times it makes me smile and gives me space to connect with my own gratitude. Connecting with you doesn't have to be complicated. The most important thing is that you make time for it and try to be present with yourself.

Connect with Community

One of the best ways to pull yourself out of a dark hole on the healing path is to remember that millions of other people are having the same experience that you're having. This is why staying connected to other spoonies is so important. You need to know that you're not alone, and it's nice to be able to laugh about the absurdity of it all sometimes.

I recommend connecting with other spoonies regularly in-person, on the phone, or whatever works for your body and mind. I'll say more about finding spoonie buddies in the coming chapters. Hanging out with other people in general, even virtually, helps you regulate your nervous system and therefore supports healing in your body.

What if you don't have a lot of people in your life? That can change! I know it can feel challenging to make new friends and connections when you're not well. You might feel extra vulnerable, risk averse, cautious about rejection, or just worried you won't have the spoons to maintain a relationship. I see you and I've been there. And many of my clients have proven over and over that you can make new friends (and all kinds of magic, really) even when you feel like total poop.

You can take it slow. I highly recommend being really clear with folks about what you can and cannot do. For example, when you are building a new relationship, don't be afraid to tell the truth up front and share things like "My energy fluctuates a lot so that means I may need to change plans a lot." Not everyone can hang with that, but you might be surprised by how many can. One upside of the global COVID-19 pandemic is that it has helped normalize people sharing that they are not okay, even with strangers, so it might even be a little easier to have these kinds of conversations now than it used to be.

Many people in this country are starved for connection and will welcome the opportunity to connect. If you are willing to try, I encourage you to put your beautiful spoonie self out there. Talk to neighbors, look for groups doing things that interest you, reach out in an online forum, or talk to someone in a yoga class, and see what happens. Some people may respond poorly or not at all, but others will be so glad you reached out!

If you cannot connect with other people in real time, there is another practice you can do to connect with folks having a similar experience. While lying down, close your eyes and bring your attention to your heart space. As you breathe, acknowledge that you are suffering and imagine other people around the world who might also be suffering in the same ways you are.

If you have MS for example, you can imagine all the other people who are also living with MS and having a particularly hard day. If you're utterly exhausted, imagine other people who might be just as exhausted. Imagine that you can tell them that you understand, and perhaps visualize holding hands with one or two of them. As you inhale, imagine sucking up all your suffering and their suffering, and as you exhale, imagine that you and everyone in the same boat as you can experience some peace and ease.

This is a variation on the Tibetan Buddhist practice of Tonglen. The word "Tonglen" means "sending and receiving" in the Tibetan language. Pema Chödrön includes a beautiful description of this practice in her must-read book, *When Things Fall Apart: Heart Advice for Difficult Times*.

Connect with Spirit

I use "spirit" as a catch-all for the divine, God, the universe, the spirits of our ancestors, the energy that connects us all, and [insert your own words here]. Cultivating a connection with spirit has a lot of perks, but I want to highlight two big ones.

First, when you feel connected to spirit, you see that you're never actually alone. Since chronic illness is really isolating, this is pretty sweet.

My friend Heather Smith introduced me to the concept of the "permacuddle." The idea is that spirit is always hugging and holding you, and you can tap into it at any moment. I think about it like being wrapped in a blanket, swaddled like an infant. Anytime you feel alone or really upset or even questioning if life is worth living, the permacuddle is there for you. Take a moment now to put the book down and see if you can feel it. It typically feels like relief, safety, love, and being held.

Second, when you're present to spirit, you see beauty everywhere. It's so much easier to get out of your own head when you're regularly experiencing awe, gratitude, and reverence for how freaking cool it is that you're alive, that plants are medicine, that the position of the moon creates tides, that a conservative Christian grandmother and her liberal trans granddaughter can love each other so much, and the list goes on.

A coach I know has a bumper sticker on their car that says, "If you're not in awe you're not paying attention." All that's required of you to experience spirit is to pay attention. Just be on the lookout for it.

If this is all new to you, that's okay. Many young people in America are spiritually bereft. We've rejected the organized religions we grew up with, or never had, so we don't have spiritual teachings, elders to guide us, or rituals to help us through our darkest moments. For white folks in the US, a lot of our ancestors renounced their spiritual traditions when assimilating into whiteness, and white supremacy has worked overtime to suppress or erase the spiritual traditions of Indigenous, Black, and other people of color in the United States in different ways.

A lot of us haven't experienced a ritual outside of weddings, funerals, baby showers, and holidays that have been commercialized and largely stripped of their meaning. As a result, some of us feel called to seek out spiritual connection and go on long journeys looking for it. Others decide they're better off without it, and others still, don't even really think about it that much. But if the resurgence in popularity of yoga, crystals, tarot, astrology, and witchcraft has demonstrated anything, it's that we are hungry for structures and ceremonies to help us understand and make meaning out of the wild times we're living in.

The cool, and often misunderstood thing about spirituality is that you can make it completely your own—but it is important to be mindful of engaging respectfully with traditions that come from outside your culture, as I explored at the end of Section 2. If you want to convert to Judaism or Islam, or go to church, join a coven, or go to a meditation center and learn Buddhist teachings, you can! But you can also just make it up. If you'd rather sit on a rock, feel the wind, and stare at the trees for a time, you can do that too. If you want to sit on the sidewalk and offer free consensual hugs to strangers, that's also fair game. The divine is everywhere. You can connect with it in any number of ways and it's up to you to figure out what works for you.

I was raised Episcopalian, and while I am grateful for what I learned of the Bible, most of it has not resonated with me. I love exploring the spiritual teachings of yoga and Buddhism and I find my deepest connection to spirit when I'm in the woods or sitting close to water. I also chant in Sanskrit sometimes, and I pray to spirit and my ancestors regularly, the way a Vodun priestess taught me to, with a lit candle and a glass of water. I wasn't given a script for the prayer. I make it up and that works for me. I also do shamanic journeys with myself. Sometimes I pull cards. Periodically, I also ask for guidance in dreams and keep a dream journal. I have found all of these to be sweet ways to connect with myself and spirit together.

I spent Labor Day weekend 2019 visiting Shelburne Falls, Massachusetts where I have lived twice, walking in the woods, sitting on rocks, weeding a friend's garden, and connecting with some of my favorite people and dog friends. It was hard to leave at the end of the long weekend. I wouldn't say I feel like I belong there, but I do feel welcome. I feel closer to spirit there in a way that I find harder to access in the city, with so many buildings and other bodies around.

Over that weekend, I spent a whole afternoon sitting on a rock by a lake, asking the wind to tell me anything I needed to know. I got lots of insight about my business, which was unexpected but welcome. Then I asked for support around how to be with a friend that I had feelings for. The response to that question came to me as a vision of a swaggery yellow grasshopper with a British accent. I had my eyes closed, so this was a vision in my mind.

The grasshopper provided guidance, answered my questions, and told me not to worry so much. It was great. I was surprised by this unusual presentation of my intuition or spirit or whatever you want to call it, but I do always try to stay open. I invite you to stay open in your journey too because messages from spirit can come in all forms. I've found that when I ask for guidance, I always get it, though sometimes it's not immediate and sometimes the vehicle for the guidance is unexpected. Practice patience and trust that spirit has your back.

Connect with the Earth

When I was at my sickest, I got really into watching birds at the birdfeeder outside the dining room window. Between all the different birds that visited, and the squirrels that tried to get in on the fun, it became pretty good entertainment and inspired me to bust out the old field guide to brush up on my bird identification skills. I also learned about migratory birds by noticing strangers at the feeder and looking them up. Call me nerdy, but it was so calming.

There is much wisdom in nature, and when we take the time to connect with it, we can gain a lot of insight, for our healing and our lives in general. You don't have to be like me and spend a bunch of time in the woods. We are all attracted to different things, and not everyone has easy access to a forest or wilderness area. Even in a city, you can get a lot from sitting on a bench for a while and observing the natural elements around you. If nothing else, almost everyone has access to the sky.

If you don't already have a nature connection practice, here are some things you might try:

- Find a spot outside where you can sit, lie down, or otherwise rest as comfortably as possible. Check in with all the senses that are accessible to you. What do you see? What do you smell? What does the ground around you feel like? Can you see animals? What are they doing? Stay as long as you can or feel called to. You might also write, draw, or make a video or audio recording about what you experience and how it makes you feel. You might choose a spot and visit there every day for a time to develop a relationship with that piece of land.
- Mindful walking. Same as above but while you're moving, if that is accessible to you.

- If weather allows, take your shoes off and put your toes in sand, dirt, water, rock, or grass. This is sometimes called "earthing" and, like everything else on this list, it will help regulate your nervous system. You can also ask the Earth to take some of your suffering for you or wash it away if you have access to water. I don't understand how it works, but sitting next to the river has dissolved migraines for me multiple times.
- If you can't leave the house (and you're not too light sensitive), set yourself up by a window and simply spend some time observing. If that's not on the table, you can try watching nature videos, listening to nature sounds, or looking at photos of plants and animals. Notice how it makes you feel in your body to have your only objective be observing the natural world. What lessons do plants, animals, and the elements have to teach you in your healing journey?

If you're a Lyme person, you might be thinking, I'd love to spend more time outside but "What about ticks?!?" A lot of folks understandably worry about the risks of being outdoors, but there are things you can do to protect yourself. When I go into the woods I make sure to wear long pants, socks and a hat that have been soaked in permethrin. I also slather myself (head, neck, ankles, and arms) in a homemade tick spray made with jojoba oil and some drops of rose geranium, eucalyptus, and garlic essential oils. It smells terrible but I wear it religiously and it works really well.

I also do tick checks and I've never found one after using this spray. If that doesn't change your reluctance to spend time outdoors, just do what you can. Like I said, even a practice of sitting or lying by a window and looking outside can help you connect with the Earth and calm your nervous system.

Connect with Your Ancestors

If you are able to learn about your ancestry, this will inevitably help you learn more about yourself. If you can learn more about the trauma your ancestors faced, it will be easier for you to recognize if and where that trauma lives in you. If you learn about how your ancestors healed themselves, it might give you information about medicine and practices that can support you in your healing.

Understanding the history of your people can also give you the warm fuzzies of connection, and help you feel like less of a weirdo. For years I thought it was weird that I was so into music because, as far as I knew, there wasn't anyone in recent generations who was musical, on either side of my family. But, at age 34, I learned that my paternal grandmother played the piano, around the same time that I acquired a keyboard.

Now, every time I play piano I feel connected to my grandmother, which somehow makes me more inclined to practice. On a super practical level, it's also just useful to know about propensities for certain illnesses and mental illnesses that run in your family lineage and/or ethnicity(ies). That knowledge might allow you to take preventative measures that will serve your physical vitality in the long run.

There are a lot of resources for researching and understanding your ancestry, like DNA tests, historical records, and websites like Ancestry. com. One of my mentors was able to trace her lineage back to West Africa and Jamaica, and then travel to those places to do additional research, experience her ancestral homelands, and build relationships with people there. But even if that's not possible, you can likely learn a lot. Of course, any living elders you have access to in your family or community might also help you get a better sense of who came before and what their lives where like.

People often feel a sense of pride when they learn more about their ancestors, but it can also be incredibly painful, especially if your ancestors were persecuted or victims of slavery or genocide. That may also mean that you don't have the same access to learning about them, which could bring its own grief. If you learn that your ancestors persecuted others or upheld oppressive systems, this can also cause feelings of grief and shame.

If you already know that your ancestry is heavy, plan accordingly and enroll support from friends, families, or healers to help you process as you learn more. Definitely do what you can to make space for whatever feelings arise to move through you and see if you can let what you learn inform and support your healing.

Clients and buddies of mine have reported being more committed to their healing once they saw themselves in the context of an ancestral line. In some cases, they felt like they owed it to their ancestors to try their best to be well, live a good life, and try to change the world so fewer would suffer going forward.

There are also classes and workshops for different ethnic groups to learn more about their heritage, and sometimes to heal their ancestral wounds. I know for white folks there are online courses, like those hosted by White Awake, to help participants connect with their ancestry, dismantle whiteness, *and* deprogram internalized white supremacy.

I am very much still on a learning journey with my ancestry and there is a lot I have yet to research. I do however feel connected to three of my grandparents in spirit, my Belgian maternal grandmother Yvonne in particular. I didn't set out to create that connection, it just sort of happened around the time I started praying regularly. While at a writing workshop for sick folks at the Omega Institute in Rhinebeck, New York I attended an evening event with a medium.[66]

As soon as I walked in the room, I had this sense that I was going to connect with Yvonne, who I called "Granny." The medium introduced herself and explained how the event would work. Dead people would speak to her. She would describe for the crowd the person who

---

66 A medium is someone who communicates with individuals who have passed on.

was speaking to her and if you thought it was your person, you were to raise your hand.

The medium would then relay a message from the deceased connection, and then move on to the next person. My grandmother ended up being the last person of the night. Her message was that my life was going to get a lot easier (great news at the time, because I had been especially sick) and that I should think of her every time I saw butterflies.

That didn't mean much to me at the time but my mother reminded me later that I'd had a really sweet visit to a butterfly house with my grandmother on one trip to Belgium. After the medium wrapped up, she motioned to me to come to the front of the room. She told me that my grandmother had a lot more to say, including that I was going to become an inspirational speaker for young women, which feels random from where I sit now, but also a cool possibility that I am open to.

While I had her attention, I asked the medium if my grandmother might be responsible for all the pennies I'd been finding. (I had been finding a lot more pennies on the street than seemed normal and one had recently turned up right in the middle of my bike seat.) She said, yes, definitely, that was very common, and I could assume the pennies were from my grandmother.

Some people will read this and think it's a crock of shit, but I'm sharing nonetheless because I think connection with ancestors can come in all forms if we're open to it. Since committing to healing, I've experienced so many synchronicities that have made me open to all kinds of magic.

The connection I have developed with my two deceased grandmothers in particular has added so much joy and ease to my life because I feel like they're always around looking out for me and taking care of me. The last two times I moved I found a penny in my rented moving truck and, with all the things that could have gone wrong during those moves, the smoothness I experienced and the support I got were a little unreal.

In the six months after moving to Somerville, MA (first time I found a penny in a moving truck), I found six pennies on the street that were minted in my birth year. The first one came in conjunction with one from my brother's birth year. At some point I was remarking to a friend that I hadn't found any pennies in a while. I was a little bummed because a friend of mine was dying and I wanted to know my grandmother was around. And I kid you not, the next day I came out of work to find three pennies on my bike seat. I am constantly in awe.

I don't really know what the pennies mean but I think it's my granny cheering me on, telling me that I'm on the right path, and encouraging me to keep going. I feel like she's around a lot but I find even more pennies when I'm dealing with something hard, or doubting that something will happen. I try to keep a regular dialogue with my grandmother, expressing gratitude for whatever is going well in my life and, when I remember, for the hard lessons too.

Sometimes I ask her for advice. I have felt the presence of my other grandmother, and her husband at different times too. One time I saw them both in a dream and my grandfather, who had a long struggle with Alzheimer's disease, gave me a very long, sweet hug as if to say that he understood how hard it was to be sick. I still weep when I think about it because I felt so seen. I treasure these connections. I feel like every time I'm struggling, some spirit shows up to remind me that I'm not alone and that life is worth living. I've been told by different healers and wise folks that we're surrounded by spirits and guides all the time, and all we have to do is start talking to them. It's certainly been fruitful for me. But the way I've connected with ancestors is just one of many ways.

In *The Spirit of Intimacy: Ancient African Teachings in the Ways of Relationships,*[67] Indigenous teacher Sobonfu Somé shares that, "…any person who has lost the physical body is a potential ancestor." I am going to share her whole section on this understanding because she says it better than I can:

> When we talk about connecting with the spirits of ancestors, many people assume that we refer to our own direct ancestors. But this is difficult. Many of us don't even know our grandfathers. There is such a thing as the pool of ancestors – it doesn't have to be a person or spirit we know or can imagine. It can be the tree out there. It can be the cows out there, your dog or cat at home. Your great-great grandfather who died many generations ago may have joined a great ensemble of spirits to the point where you can't even identify him. He's probably the creek down over there.
>
> So what is important is to realize that any person who has lost the physical body is a potential ancestor. And by simply expressing your longing for the support of ancestors, you will attract a lot of spirits.
>
> When you start a ritual where you need their support, if you address them simply as spirits or ancestors, maybe even say, 'the ones who I know, and the ones who I don't know, and those who know me more than I do myself,' you are tapping the ancestral power out there, and you are not beginning with confusion as to whether, in the pool of ancestors, there is a spirit out there you can identify with.[68]

---

67 While ostensibly about intimate relationships, this is also a GREAT book about community, connection with spirit, and ritual.

68 Sobonfu Somé, The Spirit of Intimacy: Ancient African Teachings in the Ways of Relationships (New York: Harper Collins, 1997), 15-16.

Some Suggested Practices For Cultivating Ancestral Connection:
- Ask living family members for any family trees, research, or stories they have about your ancestors. Find out if anyone in your family has done a DNA test or do one yourself to learn more about your roots.
- Make a place in your home to welcome your ancestors. This might look like an altar with objects that represent them, or photographs on a mantle.
- Light a candle and express gratitude for all that your ancestors did for you and your family. If you feel comfortable, invite them into your life, and ask for their support if you like, perhaps as Sobonfu suggests.
- Attend an event for an ethnic group you're a part of, like a Greek Festival, an Indigenous People's Day celebration, Caribbean American Heritage Festival, etc. If you do not know or cannot trace your ancestry, consider attending cultural events to learn about different rituals and traditions and notice if any of them feel familiar in your body.
- If/when you do know your ancestry, research the dances, songs, and rituals of your people. See if you can learn and practice them and notice what you feel in your body. It might bring you joy, grief, or a little bit of both. See if you can allow yourself to feel what comes up even if you don't understand it.
- If you can't find information on the rituals of your ancestors, invite them to move, talk with you, or make sound through you. Set aside some time and set the intention to let your ancestors teach you or work through you and see what happens. I have done this with sound quite a bit. I lie down and allow whatever sounds come to me to move through me and I find it incredibly cathartic.

There's no wrong way to connect with your ancestry or your actual ancestors. Like spirituality, you can make it up. The above practices are just suggestions. Play a little and see what feels interesting and useful to you. I do recommend getting yourself grounded via meditation or breathwork or whatever works for you before calling the spirits of your ancestors in. Some of my clients have reported frightening or otherwise unpleasant experiences while connecting to ancestors in spirit. This can happen. Not all of them have your best interest in mind and some of them might communicate in ways that are unsettling, such as knocking things off the wall. Don't be afraid to set boundaries with them and ask for what you want. Be clear about what you are and are not willing to receive. If you're not clear on what to say or ask for, you can ask them to *gently* share anything that would be supportive for your healing journey.

In this chapter, we've explored how to connect with yourself, with community, with the Earth, with spirit, and with your ancestors. Hopefully, you are feeling a little less isolated and have some ideas flowing about how to bring more connection into your life. I invite you to explore the questions below to reflect.

Reflection Questions:
- Where in your life would you like to experience more connection?
- What would be sweet about being more connected? What might it do for your healing?
- How might you like to connect with yourself?
- How do you love to connect with the earth?
- Try the Tonglen practice and write about how you feel afterwards.
- What do you already know and what do you want to learn about your ancestors?

Choose 1-2 bullet points to reflect on and record your answers in your healing journal.

Train Your Brain

"Free your mind and your ass will follow. The kingdom of heaven is within."

—Funkadelic

So far, you've learned how to build a foundation for healing, and how to build stronger points of connection to support the spiritual aspects of healing. Next, we'll look at the mental aspect, exploring several approaches to train your brain to support your healing. Specifically, I'll talk about limbic system retraining, observing and replacing outdated beliefs, and changing the language you use to talk about your health challenges. I'll also offer some ideas for yoga practices, mantras, and breathwork that can help you create some space between you and your thoughts. The practices outlined in this chapter will also be supportive in your journey to deprogram yourself of internalized oppression. This section includes essential tools for everyone working on collective liberation, whether they are spoonies or not. Especially in this tech-saturated society, most folks can benefit from at least some brain training.

The human brain is incredible and powerful. It can be destructive if left to its own devices. It helps to think of it like a puppy. If you train it well, you'll have a wonderful life together. If not, you'll end up with a dog that destroys your shoes, pees on the floor, jumps on people, and barks at everything. It'll be a huge headache. Same with your brain. If you just let it be, it will run you ragged with its incessant internal dialogue of doubt and worry. But with even a little training, it can be a pal, and a great ally in the healing journey.

After reading this chapter, you can choose one approach, try them all, or ignore all of these approaches if they don't resonate with you. It felt important to me that everyone on a healing journey consider brain training and know that these modalities exist. That said, these approaches are written with neurotypical brains in mind. Not all neurodivergent folks will find these practices accessible or useful, though I know that some have. If you identify as neurodivergent, please keep this in mind and know that you may need to look for resources and professionals who specifically support neurodivergent individuals. These approaches are just one avenue to healing health challenges but there are many others. I trust you to find your way.

The legendary funk band Funkadelic titled their second studio album and the first track on it, "Free Your Mind and Your Ass Will Follow." This has become a mantra for me because I've found that when we heal the mind and spirit, the body follows suit. Freeing the mind, which involves training it to slow down, focus, and get out of the way, allows the body to do what it is designed to do: repair itself. And in some ways, we have a lot more control over our mind than we do over our body.

Our body is doing its healing thing, as pleasant or unpleasant as that may be, and there's only so much we can do to control it or influence it. In contrast, we have a lot of agency when it comes to how we interpret our thoughts and emotions. We cannot control our thoughts, but we can choose how we want to be with them. And learning to observe and attend to our thoughts and emotions can produce big changes in the body.

But a mind-first approach is not for everyone. As I mentioned in earlier chapters, sometimes we need to start with the body to heal the mind; that is, free your ass and your mind will follow. We hold emotions, trauma, and ways of knowing in our bodies and sometimes addressing them from the perspective of the body first, as is done in Somatic Experiencing, is more effective than starting with the mind.

This could even look like having a three-minute dance party with yourself before trying to make a decision. Ask yourself what feels right to you and start where you feel called to start. I would not suggest starting a somatic healing modality *and* a rigorous brain training program at the same time, because they both take a lot of energy and the approaches may conflict with each other.

We have known about the power of the mind-body connection for centuries. There's a reason certain modalities like yoga, breathwork, and meditation have stuck around. You don't have to search too far to find accounts of stage four cancer patients who put their cancer in remission by meditating and pursuing what brought them joy, or well-practiced yogis who claim to have healed their own broken bones through meditation alone. That can seem far-fetched to our modern over-analytical minds but, because of the work of some brave physicians and scientists, we now have the science to prove that training our brains to chill the F out and focus on supporting the body can have a huge impact on our healing.

Back in 2003, researcher and founder of Mindfulness-Based Stress Reduction (MBSR) Jon Kabat-Zinn conducted a study on mindfulness and healing psoriasis that produced profound results.[69] Psoriasis is understood to be at least partially a genetic disorder. He split a cohort of psoriasis patients into two groups while they underwent the same treatment. One group in the study was asked to listen to a recorded meditation while undergoing treatment. The control group did not. The meditation group healed significantly faster and more fully than the control group, proving that practicing mindfulness can literally change our gene expression.

A 2013 study in Norway showed that a regular regimen of gentle yoga and breathwork, specifically the Sudarshan Kriya, results in "rapid

---

69 Jon Kabat-Zinn et al., "Influence of a Mindfulness Meditation-Based Stress Reduction Intervention on Rates of Skin Clearing in Patients with Moderate to Severe Psoriasis Undergoing Photo Therapy (UVB) and Photochemotherapy (PUVA)," Psychosomatic Medicine 60, no. 5 (1998): pp. 625-632, https://doi.org/10.1097/00006842-199809000-00020.

gene expression alterations which may be the basis for...longer term cell biological and higher-level health effects."[70]

And repeating a positive affirmation to yourself, even silently, leads to a significant slowdown of activity across the brain, including the part that is responsible for self-criticism and self-judgment.[71] That slowing down creates space for other, more nurturing attitudes, feelings, ideas, and stories to emerge. I share some of my favorite affirmations, gentle yoga poses, and breathwork practices at the end of this section so you can give them a try and notice how they affect your mind.

The field of neuroplasticity is also emerging as an exciting and must-watch scientific frontier for the spoonie community. We now know that brains can change and heal from even very traumatic injuries, and researchers have used this science to develop revolutionary therapies and treatment protocols that have helped blind people see and stroke victims regain movement in their "paralyzed" limbs.

Norman Droidge talks about these discoveries and more about the amazing powers of brain plasticity in his books. I also loved reading *The Woman Who Changed Her Brain* by Barbara Arrowsmith-Young, which includes multiple case studies of folks who completely reversed previously debilitating learning disabilities. For us spoonies specifically, there is an emerging field of practitioners creating protocols that rewire the brain in service of healing "chronic" health conditions for which there is currently no other cure.

A lot of folks with fibromyalgia and multiple chemical sensitivities (MCS), for example, are told that they should prepare to live with the conditions for life and do what they can to manage the symptoms. A Canadian patient-turned-researcher, Annie Hopper, who had severe MCS and fibromyalgia herself, figured out that both those conditions, and many others, can be caused by an impairment of the brain's limbic

---

70Su Qu et al., "Rapid Gene Expression Changes in Peripheral Blood Lymphocytes upon Practice of a Comprehensive Yoga Program," PLoS ONE 8, no. 4 (May 17, 2013), https://doi.org/10.1371/journal.pone.0061910.

71 Elizabeth Bernstein, "One Habit to Make You Happier Today," May 8, 2017, https://www.wsj.com/articles/one-habit-to-make-you-happier-today-1494259324.

system—and that such an impairment can be reversed. She found that by practicing a particular sequence of brain retraining exercises over a six-month period, patients could become symptom-free.

The limbic system is a collection of structures in the middle of the brain that regulate our behavioral and emotional responses, and particularly those related to survival, such as eating, reproduction, and staying safe. The limbic system is also involved in memory formation and integration, your sense of smell, and your autonomic nervous system, among other things.

In other words, it's kind of a big deal. When the limbic system is subjected to trauma—physical, emotional, or psychological—it stops working properly and gets stuck in a looping fight, flight, or freeze response. Because it's linked to so many systems in the body, this limbic system looping can lead to a wide range of symptoms like anxiety, depression, chronic pain, and sensitivities to food, light, smells, and sounds.

To help herself and others heal the limbic system, Hopper culled together a series of spoken and somatic exercises to create the Dynamic Neural Retraining System (DNRS), which, at the time of this writing, patients can learn at in-person trainings or via DVDs. Similar brain-retraining programs, like the Gupta Programme, Primal Trust, and Vital Side have also helped people heal from ME/CFS, mold sensitivity, adrenal fatigue, fibromyalgia and other related conditions. Unfortunately, at the time of this writing, scientific research on these programs is limited, but there is a lot of anecdotal evidence that they can help some people completely reverse previously debilitating conditions.

I'd known about DNRS for a couple years, but only decided to do it after I saw the success of my friends Sarah and Eli. The three of us all had a combination of Lyme and other conditions. At the time, Eli had been living in a tent in his mother's backyard because of severe mold and chemical sensitivities. After just a couple months of daily DNRS training, he was able to fly to New York City and hang out with his sweetie in Times Square. Given his sensitivities at the time, this seemed like a jaw-dropping miracle.

I've become something of a proselytizer for DNRS because it was such a game changer in my own healing journey. In 2012, after two years of relative wellness, I was doored by a car while riding my bicycle. I had concussive symptoms for more than two months and experienced a resurgence of Lyme symptoms that I had forgotten about. I had to pee very frequently again, I had the worst brain fog I'd ever had, and had extreme light and sound sensitivity. I couldn't go to the movies without crying during the previews because my nervous system felt completely overwhelmed, and I didn't understand why. And those were just the weirder symptoms. I was also exhausted and in pain every day.

I suffered with those symptoms and others for five years, all the while trying everything I could to feel better. Shortly after the bike crash, I recommitted to getting a Lyme diagnosis and did. I changed my diet in a big way, took antibiotics and herbs, endured a grueling parasite protocol for more than two years, and did a lot of Ondamed[72] and other alternative treatments.

While I experienced *some* healing from all that, my health didn't turn around in a big way until I did DNRS. Almost immediately after starting the program, I felt like a huge weight had been lifted off of me. DNRS helped me escape the remaining fatigue, the sound and light sensitivity disappeared, and I just generally felt physically and emotionally stronger. I also found that my personality came back, which I didn't even realize I'd lost. I felt like myself again. I laughed more and life just felt easier and brighter.

After just a few weeks of doing "rounds" of the DNRS program, I went home to Virginia for Thanksgiving. As soon as I walked through the door my mother lit up and said I looked better. For the rest of the day, she kept smiling and saying "You're better! I can't believe you're

---

72 Ondamed is a German device that diagnoses and corrects imbalances in the body using pulsed electromagnetic frequencies or PEMF. The effects of it are similar to acupuncture. Learn more about Ondamed at https://www. ondamed.net/en/.

better."[73] Some DNRS users feel big changes after just the first few days, but the program involves practicing an hour a day for at least six months for the results to stick.

It's an intense program and certainly not a good fit for everyone. It cannot be completed without serious commitment, discipline, and a certain baseline of physical and cognitive ability. To complete the program, you have to possess the spoons to do an hour of healing work a day, at least 15 minutes at a time. It's meant to be done standing but can be done sitting. If you can check those boxes, know that you also need to be willing to make changes in your life, stretch outside your comfort zone, and believe that it is going to work.

Unfortunately, brain-retraining and some of the mindfulness practices mentioned above have not yet made it into the average doctor's office. And in the meantime, patients are being told that they're stuck with what they've got. So, it's up to patients like you and me to figure out what works for us and spread the word about these new (and old) paradigms in healing.

If the concept of brain training resonates with you, definitely look up the symptoms of limbic system impairment (DNRS has a quiz to help you identify limbic system impairment on their website https://retrainingthebrain.com) and see if any of the brain retraining programs resonate with you.

Meditation can also be a good place to start because it involves training your brain to pay attention to your breath. Refer back to Section 1, Building a Strong Foundation for tips on how to get started. You can also try the mind-body practices in the following pages and see if any of them feel particularly supportive for you in calming and/or washing out your brain. If meditation doesn't work for you, the breathing practices might feel more accessible. Early in my healing journey, I took a Mindfulness-Based Stress Reduction class on my

---

73 I recorded a video in January 2020 about my experience with DNRS. Watch it on YouTube here: https://youtu.be/Hq4O-OelC40

doctor's recommendation. Six weeks in, when I told the teacher I was still having trouble meditating, she told me to stick with yoga if that worked for me. I was pissed at the time, because I'd spent $400 on the course, but yoga did turn out to be the best mindfulness practice for me at that time, and doing more of it really helped me feel better. I eventually came back to meditation and had a more enjoyable experience, probably because I'd already been practicing yoga for several years. All these practices are complementary and can be done in tandem.

Affirmations, Breathwork, and Yoga Practices

Affirmations:

Repeating affirmations slows activity across the brain and quiets feelings of self-judgment and self-criticism. If you can speak, you can practice saying affirmations out loud, perhaps while looking in the mirror, or write one down ten times each in your healing journal for multiple days. You can also repeat them silently in your mind if that is all you have access to. When you practice repeating the affirmations, notice how you feel afterwards and if it has an impact on your outlook or your behavior.

My fave affirmations:
- I am one with the universe and I will find my way
- In this moment, I am safe*
- I am healing fully**
- I release all energy that is not of my highest and best interest***

*Only use this one if it feels true. Like, I wouldn't recommend using it during a hurricane, if you're living with an abuser, or if you're in an active war zone.
**This affirmation came from Katina Makris.
***I learned this from coach, yoga teacher, and author Christie Rosen.

I also like connecting affirmations with the breath. For example, as you inhale, think or say "I am." And as you exhale, think or say, "healing fully." You can also explicitly link an intention to the breath:

- I breathe in hope. I exhale fear.
- I breathe love into my cells. I breathe out what is no longer needed.
- I breathe in to create space. I exhale to relax every fiber of my being. Or simply, "I feel my body breathe."

The practice of "Yessing," is a very simple approach to affirming your body and all of who you are. Yessing simply involves saying "yes" over and over again with every exhale and imagining that you are saying "yes" to all that is in that moment, in your body, mind, and soul. Inhale through the nose, exhale and say "yes."[74] After a while it can sound like you're having an orgasm. That's how you know you're doing it right! I usually laugh when I do it and I think that's part of the medicine. Continue for as long as desired or try setting a timer and doing it for three minutes. I recommend practicing sitting up or lying down.

Breathwork:

When meditation doesn't feel accessible or effective for me, breathwork almost always helps me shift gears and calm my mind. In yoga we practice breath control exercises called pranayama. "Prana" means life force and "ayama" means to restrain or extend. Next, I outline some pranayama practices that I feel are safe for you to practice at home. You can get a video of me demonstrating each of these if you go to the link at the beginning of the book. I recommend looking up videos on YouTube so you have a visual and/or practicing with a professional yoga teacher or breathwork teacher if and when you can. Some yoga studios offer classes and workshops that include pranayama

---

74 I don't know where this practice originated. I learned it from herbalist Tommy Priester of Bear Medicine Herbals.

instruction. More vigorous practices like Bhastrika and Kapalbhati are really powerful and best practiced with a seasoned practitioner. It is easy to overdo them.

- Ujjayi breath, also known as "victorious breath" is used to relax and energize the body. It involves a light constriction in the back of the throat. When you breathe you sound like Darth Vader in Star Wars, or the ocean. You might hear folks practicing ujjayi throughout an entire yoga class because it helps keep attention focused on the breath during asana, the physical postures in yoga. I personally like breathing normally in asana and practicing ujayii separately, sometimes on the go, when I'm out and about in the world.
- Nadi Shodana, alternate nostril breathing, helps to quiet the mind, body, and emotions. It's used to balance the nadis, or energy channels in the body. There are a couple different hand postures you can use to alternately block off your nostrils, but it can also be practiced without the finger block.
- Same-interval breathing is one of my favorites. I like to practice it in a reclined position with my upper body on a bolster or pile of pillows. Start by breathing in for the count of eight and exhaling for a count of eight. If you do a couple cycles and that feels okay, and you don't have any breathing challenges, you can add a hold for a count of eight so it becomes: breathe in for eight counts, hold for eight counts, exhale for eight counts. You do not have to do more than a few rounds to feel a tremendous impact. This practice is very grounding and good for quieting the mind. To focus on calming the nervous system, switch it up to make the exhales longer than the inhales, for example, breathe in for four counts and exhale for eight. If you feel comfortable adding a hold, see below.

- 4-7-8 breath is like same-interval breathing, but with different intervals. You breathe in for a count of four, hold for a count of seven, and exhale for a count of eight. It's a big inhale. See if you can do it softly without straining. Dr. Andrew Weil recommends practicing four cycles of 4-7-8, twice daily.[75] After a month you can increase to eight cycles, but that is the maximum recommended. The practice is helpful for mild to moderate anxiety and can help you fall asleep, even if you wake up in the middle of the night. You can use it whenever you're experiencing internal tension. When you practice this regularly, even one cycle on the go can elicit the same calming effect in the body.

Those are just a few suggestions among the many different styles of breathwork to explore. In addition to what I've learned from yoga, I have personally tried and benefitted from holotropic breathwork, effiji, and David Elliott's breathwork as taught by his students. Many of my friends and clients have also benefited from Wim Hof's breathwork. It hasn't felt like a good fit for me and my nervous system, but I wanted to mention it so you can explore it as an option. All of these are very vigorous practices, with David Elliott's probably being the gentlest. They can be painful and intense. I recommend really checking in with yourself before signing up for a class. Ashley Neese's book, *How to Breathe: 25 Simple Practices for Calm, Joy, and Resilience* is an excellent introduction to breathwork generally, with many practices that you can do safely on your own.

Yoga:

As I mentioned, yoga has been a tried and true practice for mindfulness and healing for me for a long time. There are many different

---

75 I like this video example made by Dr. Andrew Weil: https://www.drweil.com/videos-features/videos/breathing-exercises-4-7-8-breath/

yoga traditions and styles which you can explore, but even if you never become someone who does yoga regularly, you might enjoy and benefit from some of the poses. If yoga doesn't speak to you, you might explore Tai Chi or Qigong as other avenues for cultivating mind-body connection and a calmer, more focused mind.

Here are a few of my favorite yoga poses and practices for calming the mind:

- Viparita Kirani at the wall is a super powerful restorative pose that involves lying on the floor with your legs up the wall. It is great for the lymphatic system and boosts energy. I do it almost every day, sometimes multiple times a day. Someone told me once that 20 minutes of viparita kirani does the same for your body as two hours of sleep. I don't have science to back that up, but I do find it to be a helpful boost when I'm really tired. I'll do it in the morning after I wake up, at the office, or to reset between coaching calls. To get into the pose, sit next to the wall with one hip and shoulder right up against the wall. Then lie your head and torso down on the floor and carefully rotate to put your legs straight up the wall so you are making an "L" shape with your body. I like to use a towel, blanket, or folded yoga mat as padding under my torso. Be sure to come out of this pose slowly.

- Yoga Nidra, or "yogic sleep," gets you into the state between sleeping and being awake. It's incredibly relaxing, restorative, and can also serve as a devotional practice of surrendering to the divine. One of my spoonie buddies takes yoga nidra "naps" every day in the late morning to help her get through the day. Look for yoga nidra recordings online or on the Insight Timer app to help you recharge through the day or relax before bedtime. Yoga Nidra is sometimes offered in workshops or as part of restorative yoga classes. I recommend calling your local studio and seeing if any of the teachers offer yoga nidra as part of their classes.

- Restorative Yoga saved my life. People teach it differently, but my favorite restorative classes involve little more than lying on bolsters and blankets in different shapes designed to relax and restore the body and regulate the nervous system. Sometimes restorative yoga is offered in conjunction with reiki, where teachers or assistants give you energy work while you're resting, which makes for an extra sweet and rejuvenating experience.
- Yin Yoga is more challenging than restorative, but also often more accessible for some people than the more active vinyasa yoga. It comes out of Chinese Medicine and can be really good for people with POTS or other forms of dysautonomia, because it doesn't involve all the up and down movements of vinyasa. In Yin, you hold each pose for a longer period of time and you can transition between poses in ways that work for your body. I did Yin almost exclusively for more than a year when I couldn't practice vinyasa. I found that it helped me build strength and focus my mind without worrying that I would black out mid-class due to dysautonomia.

Reflection Questions & Exercise:
- When you read about the practices above, what sounds appealing to you? In your healing journal, write down 1-3 practices that you're willing to try in the next few weeks.
- Pick one activity you can do on your own. Put this book down and try it right now. Notice if/how it shifts your energy and record what you experience in your healing journal.
- Who could you ask to try one of these practices with you, in person or virtually?

Interrogate Your Mental Models

Now that I've offered some strategies for calming the mind, I want to say a little more about how to actually train your brain to be an ally in your healing journey. I will share strategies for observing and shifting your thinking that you can apply to both your physical healing as well as your efforts to deprogram internalized oppression.

What I offer here is greatly informed by my coaching training with the Academy for Coaching Excellence, which was heavily influenced by Buddhist teachings about working with the mind. I have deep gratitude and appreciation for these teachings because of what they have allowed me to achieve in my own healing, and for how they have helped me support so many others in theirs.

If what I share in this next section resonates with you, you might enjoy learning more about Buddhist teachings on the subject. Mind training is a powerful practice for living in alignment with the land, with the divine, with your values, and your deepest desires. Living in alignment in our culture requires overcoming a lot of critical or limiting internal conversations, and in this section, I'll offer a framework for doing just that.

Having coached a lot of folks with health challenges over the years, I've noticed common themes in what my clients are longing for and what is holding them back. Many of the clients I've worked with have been dancers who were not dancing when we met, for example. A second common theme is a deep desire to live closer to the land—to spend more time in nature, to live outside, work on a farm, or something in that vein.

Also common is a desire for more community and deeper connection with others. I've seen in my clients' and my own experience that when those longings are met, even in small ways, that starts to create harmony in the body and mind. Then healing happens faster and with more ease. I find this interesting because folks often think they can't dance or live closer to the land or spend time with people they love precisely *because* they're sick and/or disabled. I often hear comments such as "I can't dance because it makes me flare up." This plays into a dominant narrative in the chronic illness community that our health separates us from connection and what we really love.

In reality, illness invites us to slow down, move through the world in a different way, and come back to who we really are as humans. It invites us to live and connect with others in ways that are more resonant with our biology and our deepest desires. Illness invites us to dance in different ways than we might have before.

I hear some of you saying, "But Noëlle, if I go to a dance class, I'll be in bed all day tomorrow." I hear you, *and* dancing full out in a class is not the only way to access dance. Dancing seated, dancing with your fingers or simply visualizing yourself dancing can have some of the same positive effects on your body and mind as dancing hard in a class for an hour.

There are also dance programs and classes specifically for people with health challenges and disabilities. One of my clients joined Abilities Dance, an inclusive dance troupe in Boston for folks with and without disabilities. That client not only found ways to safely and comfortably dance but also perform publicly, which has been enormously empowering for them.

Our actions are informed by our thoughts, and our thoughts are informed by our belief systems. If life isn't going the way you'd like, healthwise or otherwise, it can be useful to check and see if your belief system needs an upgrade. We've all been programmed by our family and society to believe certain things, and even though our beliefs usually evolve when we age, we often unconsciously hold on to old belief systems and may not even realize that they are holding us back. It's not bad, it's just a thing we humans do.

So, it can be useful to look under the hood from time to time and see if the voices in your head actually match up with your vision and personal truths. One of my favorite aspects of coaching is that it provides the opportunity for people to vocalize some of their internal conversations (which doesn't happen much in other contexts) so they can realize how silly, ridiculous, outdated and/or untrue certain thoughts actually sound. We're going to look together at how you can start to watch your thoughts and identify thought patterns that are no longer serving you, including thought patterns informed by societal programming you received as a young one.

As we grow up, the brain naturally develops conclusions about who we are, how other people behave, and what we need to do to survive, and the brain creates systems for organizing and filtering new information as it comes to us. We create these mental models about everything, including what it means to be healthy, what it means to be successful, what kind of work we should be doing, what being a good parent looks like, etc. Wikipedia says of mental models, "It is a representation of the surrounding world, the relationships between its various parts and a person's intuitive perception about their own acts and their consequences."[76]

Our mental models are informed by our surroundings and therefore include all kinds of internalized oppression passed down to us from our families, communities, and society at large. If you ever find yourself thinking that your internal conversations are especially brutal or messed up, please know that you are not special. We have all been programmed to believe wildly untrue things about humans, the earth, and how the world works. Try not to judge yourself.

Mental models aren't necessarily good or bad, or even always limiting, but sometimes it's worth taking a look at them and seeing if they feel aligned and are still serving us. Often when we feel stuck in life, there's an outdated mental model that's getting in our way. For example, you could unconsciously be telling yourself, "I want to be an artist but, because of my training, I should be a scientist," blocking

76 "Mental Model," Wikipedia, March 15, 2023, https://en.wikipedia.org/wiki/Mental_model.

yourself from exploring art at all. Orienting yourself to "shoulds" this way causes suffering because it keeps you from doing what you know in your heart is yours to do, whether that is to play guitar instead of baseball or see an acupuncturist instead of a surgeon. And that "should"-related suffering can really limit your healing.

If you've been sick for a long time, you've probably developed a whole set of mental models about being sick and what that means. Some common spoonie beliefs include:[77]

- Because I'm ill, no one will date me and I'll never have a partner.
- I cannot have a fulfilling career as a sick person.
- I have to focus on myself so much that I'm not contributing enough to others.
- I've already tried everything and none of it worked, so no treatment is going to work.
- This is my fault.
- Other people will never be able to understand what I'm going through.
- If I just work hard enough I'll be able to fix this.
- I should be able to figure this out on my own. Because I haven't, I've failed.
- I'm no fun. No one wants to hang out with me when I'm like this.
- I can't afford what I want/need to heal.
- Other people have it easier.
- Other people have more support than I do.

---

77 Shoutout to my DNRS buddies and fellow coaches Eli Grobel and Sarah Regenspan for helping me build this list.

- This whole experience is a derailment from what my life was supposed to look like.
- I can't possibly keep working and heal because I can't work without being stressed.

More general examples of limiting beliefs from outdated mental models include:

- All artists are broke and starving.
- I'm just not a math person.
- I don't have time for…
- My boss is just a jerk who doesn't respect me.

As real as these notions can feel, they're rarely the truth, and many of them are shaped by ableist and capitalist cultural norms. The first bullet point above about dating is especially common, but I have personally had many lovely, committed partnerships even when I've been really sick. If some of these mental models and beliefs sound familiar to you, don't despair. Join the club! Our minds are very intelligent when it comes to keeping us safe. At some point, it was intelligent and useful to you to see the world through some of these mental models. And maybe they're not serving you anymore. Old mental models could be keeping you from seeing new possibilities as well as experiencing ease and joy in your healing.

Learning to recognize a mental model that isn't working for you can be a liberating experience. As soon as you see it, and see that it is not true for you, you can choose to be more interested in creating a new mental model—one that feels true and serves the vision you have for your life. Then you can make a point of collecting evidence to support this new, more supportive conclusion. This is very much not an argument for just thinking positively. It's about observing and questioning your thought patterns and upgrading them as needed.

Because our thoughts shape our behavior, if you find yourself struggling to give up a bad habit or form a new one, it could be because an old mental model is getting in the way. For example, let's say one of your practitioners recommended a new protocol two weeks ago but you have yet to start it. You might start by asking yourself, what internal conversation is keeping me from doing this? What is in the way? It could be helpful to write about it or talk about it. Then you might see that what's coming up is the common spoonie mental model, "I've tried everything, and it never makes a difference, so why bother?"

If your attention is on "why bother?", no wonder you haven't started! So even though that's what's coming up, first acknowledge yourself: "Honey, I know you've been working your butt off and not getting the results you want and that's super sucky. I hear you and I love you." Then ask yourself, "Even so, why might this protocol be worth trying? What possibility could emerge from giving this a shot? How does this protocol feel different?" Then you might remember that this protocol takes a unique and totally different approach than anything else you've tried, so it's possible that it could be more effective. Is that a possibility you're willing to entertain?

Cultivating the ability to identify and let go of an outdated mental model, and collect evidence for a new one, will support you in taking actions that are informed by and aligned with the vision you have for your healing and your life. In the coaching model I'm trained in we call this coherence.[78] Acting in alignment with your vision and values is practicing coherence. Acting in ways that are not in alignment creates incoherence. Some symptoms of incoherence (acting out of alignment) include frustration, resignation, and cynicism.

When you're acting in ways that are coherent (in alignment with your deepest truths), you experience satisfaction, meaning, fulfillment, and harmony. Sometimes the best next move you can make in your

---

78 This is the Academy for Coaching Excellence coaching model created by Dr. Maria Nemeth. Learn more at https://acecoachtraining.com/ and in Dr. Nemeth's book, Mastering Life's Energies: Simple Steps to a Luminous Life at Work and Play.

healing is an action that restores coherence. This could look like quitting smoking, leaving a relationship that's not serving you, or making an appointment you've been avoiding. Asking myself where I'm at on the coherence/incoherence barometer in any particular moment has been enormously helpful in my own healing. When I notice I'm frustrated, I can ask myself, "Am I taking coherent actions? How might I be out of alignment right now?"

Consider this possibility: You wake up one morning with more energy than usual and consider going for a bike ride. Some part of you knows that going for a bike ride will sap all your spoons and keep you from going to a friend's birthday party tonight that you've been looking forward to for a long time. But your mind has a lot of evidence for why going for a bike ride is definitely the right choice, "It's good to get exercise. I'm sick of sitting around. It's nice outside. I have to start getting fit again or I'll never feel good about my body." That voice wins, you push yourself to bike for 30 minutes, and you end up on the couch for the rest of the day because it was too much too fast for your body. You miss your friend's birthday party and feel bummed that your body can't do all the things that some other bodies do. This is an example of incoherence causing suffering.

We all do incoherent things all the time, and often they're informed by old mental models or outdated conclusions. It's not something to judge yourself for, but instead is something you can start bringing awareness to. The more aware you are, the easier it is to catch yourself and make more coherent choices. If you've been practicing the art of observing your thoughts, you might be able to step back, see this happening in your mind and catch yourself. To continue the last example, before rushing to go for a bike ride, you might check in with yourself and choose instead to go for a short walk, because it's actually more important to you to see friends tonight than start a new fitness routine. That's choosing coherence.

Incoherence is natural, *and* a huge contributor to human suffering. The more you act in ways that are incoherent, out of alignment with your deepest truths, the more life is going to feel hard, maybe excruciating, or at the very least, super mediocre. It will also feel as if your dreams, like a desire to experience a different level of physical vitality, are always out of reach. But the promise of this mind training practice is acting more coherent more of the time, which not only saves energy but yields more desirable results. Of course, there will still be external forces that make life difficult and excruciating at times, but evaluating your mental models and noticing when you are being incoherent helps bring some ease to managing what *is* within your control.

One of my clients, after doing a lot of good observing and shifting of her thoughts and behavior, texted me "It's all happening. Coherence is amazing! I love you and I love this life!" This is a common sentiment amongst my clients once they have some experience with this practice. When you are more coherent more of the time, the shifts you experience in your life can feel like magic. Most of us have no idea just how much our minds are holding us back. When we can get old mental models out of the way, the results can feel significant and surprising.

Sometimes my clients try to beat themselves up for their particular mental models and I like to gently remind them that they didn't decide to be self-limiting, racist, ableist, or constantly worried about money. Our mental models are, of course, shaped by the people who raised us, and society at large. And what's cool is that we don't actually need to know where our mental models come from in order to let them go. We can just decide they're not working and give them the boot. That said, I've found that when we can label certain beliefs and ways of knowing as the influence of kyriarchy then it is that much easier to let them go. When you've believed something for a long time, perhaps your whole life, it's unlikely that you can completely detox it from your system overnight. But, if every time a certain thought comes up, you can remind yourself that it's not yours and it's not true (for example, thinking you always need to be productive is just an internalized capitalist social construct), it becomes that much easier to redirect your attention to what is true for you.

It is important for us in the chronic illness crowd to see when we're holding ourselves up to societal standards that really don't make sense for us given where we're at healthwise. A lot of our mental models can be traced back to American cultural narratives around what success looks like and what we should be able to accomplish, by ourselves, without help from anyone else. Just a short survey of common Americanisms shows us how misleading and damaging our dominant cultural narratives are.

The pull-yourself-up-by-your-bootstraps trope, for example, implies that everyone in America has an equal shot at going from rags to riches without any kind of support. In short, if you work hard enough, you can achieve all your dreams and material wealth. In today's reality, when so many people are not paid a living wage and 63 percent of Americans live paycheck to paycheck,[79] people can literally work themselves to death without achieving the American dream.

People with generational wealth, particularly white folks, have a leg up to accumulate wealth, own property, or start businesses and, no matter who you are, most people who build and own things here get some support along the way from their community, family, government programs, or otherwise. The popular narrative of going it alone gaslights people into thinking it's their fault that they're not rich or in perfect health. This harmful narrative degrades community by encouraging individualism and competition. In reality, we are organisms who need support, and each other, to survive.

In addition to being prone to hyper-independent thinking, we also put a lot of pressure on ourselves to be "normal." The word "normal" as used to describe a person or body didn't enter the English language

---

79 Jessica Dickler, "63% Of Americans Are Living Paycheck to Paycheck - Including Nearly Half of Six-Figure Earners," CNBC, October 24, 2022, https://www.cnbc.com/2022/10/24/more-americans-live-paycheck-to-paycheck-as-inflation-outpaces-income.html.

until around 1840[80] and it came out of a school of European 19th century statisticians who happened to be eugenicists. Eugenics promotes the idea of creating a "more superior" human race by favoring certain genetic groups over others, to be achieved by controlled breeding. Eugenicists promoted the idea of "normal" as associated with "the average man," which was of course a man, first of all, and totally Eurocentric. There is no such thing as normal. It's a white supremacist, colonialist, ableist construct. Some bodies don't need to rest a lot. Others do and that's okay. They are just as worthy of love and support and should be valued just the same as other bodies. Remember this if you find yourself wishing you "could just be normal."

Another harmful trope that's hurting us is our obsession with "productivity." We can trace this back to the early British colonists, who brought the idea of the Protestant work ethic with them to Turtle Island. The Protestant work ethic grew out of a belief that hard work and frugality were indicators of who was predestined to be saved (get into heaven). Since they didn't really know who was predestined, the dominant culture promoted these ideals.

This idea was foundational to the U.S.'s particular brand of racial capitalism, which enslaved Black people and committed genocide against Indigenous people in a quest to accumulate profit. These ideas are still harming us today. As Tricia Hersey of The Nap Ministry outlines in *Rest as Resistance: A Manifesto*, capitalism has brainwashed us into thinking we have to work at a machine-level pace, "feeding into the same engine that enslaved millions into brutal labor for its own relentless benefit."[81] There's no science that says you have to work hard to be a happy, healthy human being. If this is something you've struggled with, perhaps seeing that "being productive" is a social construct might allow yourself to rest with a little more ease. I've seen this happen with my clients a lot.

---

80 L. J. Davis, The Disability Studies Reader (Routledge, 1997).

81 "Rest Is Resistance" (Little Brown Spark, February 7, 2023), https://www.littlebrownspark.com/titles/tricia-hersey/rest-is-resistance/9780316365215/?utm_source=author&utm_medium=social&utm_campaign=restisresistance.

When we commit to recognizing and letting go of mental models that grew out of these cultural narratives, or any mental models that aren't serving us, we create the opportunity to hear and follow our own hearts with more clarity, thereby boosting our body's healing ability. It's awesome to do this work with the support of a coach, counselor, a coaching/counseling group, or even a group of friends, but you can start practicing with yourself anytime.

EXERCISE:

Get a fresh piece of paper and make four columns labeled A, B, C, and D.

In Column A, write down a few things you'd like to do in your life, like some things on your bucket list. Read the list and notice what feelings and inner dialogue come up.

In Column B, write down all the reasons you feel you can't do or can't have the things in Column A. What feels impossible? And why is it impossible? Write these down. These may shed light on some of the mental models that inform your thinking.

Then, in Column C, for each reason you've listed, ask yourself, "Who is saying this right now?" Is this message coming from a panicked reptilian brain operating on survival instincts? Is it something your mom would say? Are you holding yourself up to a societal norm? Is it internalized ableism?

And, regardless of who is saying it, is it 100% true? If you see that something logically isn't true but it still *feels* really true, that can be a good belief to bring to a coach, counselor, or even a trusted friend. If you see the belief/story/excuse is not true, or not totally true, reflect on and write about that. What makes it not 100% true?

Go through these questions for every item on your list.

Then in Column D, for each thing on your list, answer the question: What could I do if this wasn't the truth? For example, if you didn't believe that you would always be too sick to travel the world, what might you be doing now to support you in traveling in the future?

Bonus Writing Exercise: If you find some mental models that you feel done with, ask yourself, "What is a new mental model or belief that I'd like to try on?" If, for example, you feel done with the belief that you have to work a desk job to survive, what alternative ways of earning income are you interested in exploring? Let yourself dream big and record any possibilities you see.

If you ask yourself where you'd like to shift your attention and the answer isn't immediately clear, that is okay. Put the question up somewhere you can see it and trust that the answer will come to you. It's not unusual, after being sick for a long time, to feel unclear and disconnected from your heart's desires and what really matters to you. Desires and values will also change as you heal and grow.

I recommend regularly revisiting the healing vision you wrote in the Building a Strong Foundation Section to remind yourself what you *do* know you want. Remember that you can revise your vision as you travel on the healing path. Regularly practicing the exercises in the upcoming Strengthen Your Intuition section will allow you to continue to clarify what you're all about and act accordingly.

The Language of Healing

The words we use can have a powerful impact on our healing, either to expand or to limit its possibilities. Being intentional about the language we use is another way to practice coherence and attune the brain to healing. As part of the process of deprogramming ourselves of oppressive constructs, we need to check that our speech reflects our inner values.

Every time we utter a word, we have the opportunity to wage war or love on ourselves and others. Since beating up on our bodies and ourselves is so widely accepted and even encouraged in our culture, most of us learn to speak ill of ourselves regularly without even realizing it.

Do you or people in your life apologize for every little thing, and perhaps emphasize an apology with phrases like, "I'm the worst?" This negation of ourselves and our experience reinforces conscious and unconscious thoughts that can keep us from healing in mind, body, and spirit. Even the way we talk about how we're feeling can reinforce our mindset, good or bad.

When you say you feel like "crap," you're reinforcing and strengthening the crap feeling. The same thing can happen when you talk about your symptoms a lot. By talking about them, you're giving them attention and power. Again, like adrienne maree brown says, what you pay attention to grows. I'm not saying don't speak your truth, but you can be intentional about the language you use to express your experience. You can acknowledge your symptoms without letting them completely hijack your attention. In this section we'll look at how you might observe and shift your language to better support your healing.

I've been lucky enough to have practitioners who felt very strongly about using pro-healing language and it was a chiropractor who first brought the power of word choice to my attention. I was explaining to him that I felt "gross" in the mornings when I woke up. He said to me, with a smile on his face, "I've worked on some truly gross people. You are not gross. It's time to stop using that word." He encouraged me to try something gentler, like "I am feeling physically challenged in the mornings."

In our society, paradoxically but perhaps unsurprisingly, the language of healing is riddled with the language of war. It's anything but gentle and the violence is so pervasive we don't even realize it. She is "battling" cancer. He is a "Lyme warrior." They are "fighting" this disease. It's not surprising given our country's legacy of colonialism and ongoing militarism around the world. But last time I checked, violence wasn't conducive to healing. And violent speech can be just as injurious as violent action.

It's going to be important that you not speak poorly of other beings or yourself during your healing process, and that includes every part of yourself. Waging war is not a good healing strategy. It is energy sucking rather than energy enhancing. If your focus is on "beating" the bacteria, cancer, virus, injury, etc., two things are working against you.

First, your focus is on that thing—the cancer, virus, or injury—rather than on getting your body strong and healthy enough to heal said thing. Second, you are distracted from listening to your internal guidance. The language of war is externally focused and depleting. Healing comes with an internal focus and a restoration of harmony in the body. As is said in Traditional Chinese Medicine, energy follows focus.

Then there's "getting better." That's what so many people want, right? To get better? I know I did for a long time. But better than what? As long as we're trying to get better, we're coming from a place of lack, of scarcity, and not being enough. This can perpetuate a mindset in which you don't have agency in your healing—the opposite of what we want. I want you to claim and feel your agency!

Another common self-denigrating word choice is "normal," as in, "I'm not normal" or, "I just want to be normal." As I mentioned earlier, the concept of a normal body was invented by eugenicists. What the hell is normal? Normal according to whom? Normal like you want to fit more squarely into white supremacist capitalist constructs? I wouldn't think so.

Normal and not normal is a false binary that helps preserve patriarchy, capitalism, white supremacy, and other oppressive systems and constructs. There is no normal. Different bodies have different needs—and given that more than 60% of the population lives with a chronic health challenge, living without health challenges isn't even technically the norm. It's an ableist myth.

If you're reading this and thinking, "Shit, I say all of these things," know that all is well. You're perfect, *and* it might be a good time to come up with some new verbiage, and let semantics be your ally in healing. Start by thinking about how you want to describe your experience with chronic illness. You can name your experience however you like, but I recommend choosing something that feels empowering to you.

You might declare that you are "in recovery" or "on a healing journey." Call yourself a healing hero, a healing badass, or a wizard lizard. It really doesn't matter, as long as it feels true to you. One of my practitioners, after a year of working together, said that I was no longer allowed to call myself a "sick" person. He told me I could say that I was "healing" or "in recovery" and he encouraged me not to mention Lyme disease by name if I could help it. I started telling people simply that I was on a healing journey, and I found this empowering.

These days, I'm in a different place with it. I'll say, "I had a long journey with Lyme disease," or, "I've been on a healing journey for more than 20 years," because it no longer feels like a bummer. I'll also just say that I'm disabled because it feels true and not a bummer. My healing journey has been a big part of my life and I want to honor that. It has definitely shaped who I am and I have seen that being open about my experience gives other people an opportunity to share their story, or ask about mine for their own benefit.

Folks who are familiar with the Dynamic Neural Retraining System (DNRS) already know that shifting the language you use to talk about your body and symptoms is a big part of rewiring your brain for healing. DNRS provides specific alternatives so you can communicate in a truthful but neutral way. Instead of saying that you're "feeling bad," "sick," or specifically mentioning any symptoms, you are to refer to your symptoms only as "its" and "pops," unless you're at a doctor's appointment.

You can also say that you're feeling "challenged." Like talking about "spoons" or calling yourself a "spoonie," this approach allows you to communicate honestly while sparing your brain the emotional energy suck that happens when you talk about diagnoses or symptoms in detail. If you've ever been in a poorly run chronic pain or illness support group meeting, you have experienced the extreme end of this energy drain.

If there are no boundaries or shared agreements, it quickly becomes a deep well of despair and/or a competition for who can make their experience sound the worst. I don't blame folks for that. I think it's a natural reaction to being regularly dismissed or erased, and without enough outlets for sharing our truths. But it's also a lot to stay present to.

In addition to influencing your own experience, the words you use can have huge implications on your interactions with others. The question of how to be real about how you're feeling without making other people uncomfortable comes up all the time in the chronic illness community. One common approach is to lie and say you're fine a lot, operating on the assumption that people don't want to know or can't handle the truth.

There's a common worry about being a downer— that if you share your truth, people will perceive you as negative, or at the very least a bummer, and will start to avoid you. There are always going to be people who can't handle discomfort, yours or their own, but choosing new words to describe your reality might actually allow you to be truthful, and build deeper, more authentic connections with others. So, when someone asks, "how are you?" how *might* you reply authentically without getting into all the details? You might record a few ideas in your healing journal.

Personally, I love nothing more than when someone tells me they're having a challenging day, because I know they're being real with me. It's so refreshing! And I, as the receiver, still get to choose whether or not I engage with that further or not. I can ask, "Do you want to say more about that?" or I can simply say, "I'm sorry to hear that" and then ask what's for lunch. We forget sometimes that we, as speakers and listeners, have agency over what we do and don't talk about. You get to have boundaries, baby!

I invite you to be curious about the words and phrases you regularly use to talk about how you feel. What do you notice about them? Are they draining? Empowering? Neutral? And, while you're at it, how are you talking about yourself and your accomplishments more generally? Are you giving yourself credit for the things you are doing and how you are being? How often are you putting yourself down or diminishing yourself?

Just like giving your symptoms a lot of airtime, self-criticism and excessive humility will reinforce ideas about yourself that do not serve your healing. Be on the lookout for language, stories, and scripts that you can reword or replace to be more supportive. It's important to make sure that the new ones still feel true. We can't force ourselves to believe something that's not true, so I'm not suggesting that you trade out "I'm the worst" for "I'm the best."

You could do that, but it doesn't work unless at least part of you believes it. I recommend starting small. Let's say you notice that you've been describing symptoms or diagnoses with the word "my." For example, "my endometriosis" or "my pelvic floor pain." Start by swapping "my" for "the." This could sound like "the IBS is acting up today" instead of "my IBS is acting up." If you can, just for kicks, say both of those sentences out loud right now. Do you notice a different energy in one sentence versus another? It's a small shift with a big impact.

I heard renowned meditation teacher and author Sharon Salzberg address this in regard to her knee on an episode of the *CTZN Podcast*.[82] She pointed out that it was just inaccurate to say she had a "bad" knee. Her knee didn't do anything wrong. It didn't deserve to be labeled "bad." More accurately, it was "having a challenge." Choosing

---

82 Kerry Kelly, interview with Sharon Salzburg, CTZN Podcast, podcast audio, May 19, 2018, https://www.ctzn-well.org/ctznpodcast/sharon-salzberg

to change even one word in your vocabulary could have a huge impact on your healing.

Like most things related to healing, cultivating awareness around your diction is nice to get support with. We can only be so self-aware, especially if we are low on spoons. I recommend asking friends, family, or anyone you communicate with regularly to reflect back to you what they're hearing, reading, or seeing you say, with particular attention to any words or phrases that sound injurious to yourself, or that sound like they are reinforcing your health challenge(s). Having your words reflected back to you can be illuminating. You can also ask others to gently call you out when you use words or phrases that you're seeking to eliminate from your vocabulary.

Several years ago, I was speaking with my roommate at the time about how folks socialized as women frequently over-apologize. We decided that was a bunch of bullsh*t, and we pledged to stop saying "sorry" unless we were genuinely making an apology. We established a fee-for-use system so that whenever one of us said "sorry" the other would say "quarter!" and the perpetrator would have to put a quarter in a "sorry jar."

It was a great way to support each other to build awareness around our words. We pledged to use the money in the jar for our party fund, but after a while, we didn't even need the jar. Just saying "quarter!" helped us keep our unnecessary "sorrys" in check. We learned to use new words in place of "sorry" and the practice has stuck. When I accidentally bump into someone, for example, or I'm interrupting someone to ask a question I'll say "excuse me" or "pardon me." Getting support on this front really works. Ask folks to help you out. If you have a relationship with a therapist, coach, mentor, or counselor, ask for their help to bring awareness to and switch up the language you use.

Once you identify words you're no longer interested in using, choose substitutes that feel authentic and empowering to you. Here are some of my favorite substitutions to get you started. You'll notice that some are direct and some are more passive. This assumes that there are some folks in your life who you feel more comfortable being direct with than others. Also, it's always nice to have options. I encourage you to experiment, try some on, see what feels good, and develop your own healing language.

Examples of Language Swaps:

Familiar language:	What you could say instead:
"I'm flaring."	"I'm feeling challenged today."
"I feel like garbage."	"I'm moving a little more slowly today."
	"I could use some extra support today."
	"I'm going to be a little less perky today."

Familiar language:	What you could say instead:
"I have MS."	"I'm healing from…"
"I have Lyme Disease"	"I'm recovering from…"
	"I'm a [illness] survivor."
	"I live with health challenges."
	"I'm on a (healing) journey with…"
	"I'm disabled."

Familiar language:	Alternate Language:
"I am [anxious, depressed, exhausted, etc.]"	"I am experiencing anxiety."
"My POTS is acting up."	"The [diagnosis/symptom] is acting up today."

Familiar language:	Alternate Language:
I have a bad knee.	My knee is feeling challenged.
	I experience pain in my knee sometimes.
	I am healing a knee injury.

Talking this way may feel cheesy or foreign at first. That is just your brain resisting a change to the status quo. It's normal. Stick with it. Notice how you *feel* when you use different language and notice how others *react* to you.

If, like me, you want to live in a world in which people feel safe to authentically share how they are feeling, physically and otherwise, you might also shift the way you greet other people and ask them questions. For example, if you hate the question "how are you?" try out something else. Some of my buddies will ask, "how is your heart?" as an invitation for the other person to share how they are feeling emotionally. Jenni Grover, author of *ChronicBabe 101: How to Craft an Incredible Life Beyond Illness*, used to sign her newsletters "Be AWAP." AWAP is an acronym for "as well as possible"—acknowledging that us spoonies can't just "be well," as many wish us to be, but we can strive to be as well as possible. I started using that for even non-spoonies when the

COVID-19 pandemic started because few people were "well" and it felt wrong to say, "I hope you are well."

One last thing about healing and language: Sometimes folks are resistant to calling themselves a "healer" when they are not in a professional or official healing capacity. But I invite you to think about it more expansively.

When you are committed to your healing, others take notice and are inspired to heal themselves, which pretty much makes you a healer. And, if you *do* aspire to help others heal, professionally or otherwise, you must be on the healing path yourself. But even if you're only focused on yourself at the moment, you're a healer in the sense that you're mastering the art of healing and you want your actions, thoughts, *and* speech to reflect that. So, try it on. Call yourself a healer and see how it feels.

EXERCISE:

Brainstorm two to four situations in which you might be asked to talk about your health. In your healing journal, write down what you'd typically say in response. Then reflect:

- What do you notice about your responses?
- Do you see words that you'd like to swap out?
- How would you *love* to introduce yourself and your health reality going forward?

Write out a new intro, maybe for a couple for different situations. For example, if I need to talk about my health in the workplace I might say, "I live with health challenges that require lifestyle shifts and accommodations." If it feels helpful, you might write some new language you want to practice and hang it up somewhere where you can see it, as a reminder. Talk to people in your life about your desired shift and ask for their support.

Bonus exercise: How do you want to answer the question "How are you?" And how might your answer change in different settings, such as with a friend or family member vs. a co-worker or someone you meet on the street?

Should You Identify as Disabled?

To go a step deeper in our exploration of how to talk about health challenges, I want to specifically explore why spoonies should consider identifying as disabled. I'll talk about why people with chronic illness can benefit tremendously from being in community with disabled folks and how, together, we can build more power and access.

Based on how few people even in my liberal Boston bubble knew the definition of the word "ableism" when I started writing this book in 2017, my assumption is that many people across America are not yet familiar with the term, which describes discrimination in favor of able-bodied people.

Unless you are disabled or know an openly or visibly disabled person, it's unlikely that access challenges and the exclusion or inclusion of disabled people are something you think about every day.

If that's you, don't despair. All is well. Take a deep breath and keep reading. I still have a lot to learn about disability justice myself and am by no means an expert. I am grateful to my community for their support in furthering my education, and I continue to learn a lot from the work of disability (justice) activists, educators, and cultural workers like Mia Mingus, Kevin Gotkin, Riley Dwight, Alice Wong, Naomi Ortiz, Leah Lakshmi Piepzna-Samarasinha, and Sins Invalid, a disability justice performance project that centers people of color, queers, nonbinary and trans people with disabilities and maintains a very useful disability justice primer. I share additional resources at the end of this chapter.

It may seem like being focused on healing and calling yourself "disabled" are at odds, but I want to argue the contrary. People with chronic illness and otherwise disabled individuals have a lot to gain from being in community with each other. I first started to understand this by lurking in the Bay Area Sick & Disabled Queers Facebook group. I have never lived in the Bay Area, but someone once suggested I post in there about my coaching and I observed so much beautiful sharing and support and community validation in the group.

Even though I'd been sick for more than a decade at this point, this was the first time I'd seen a community use both the "sick" and "disabled" identifiers together (disabled brilliance at work!). It just makes sense for these overlapping communities to be able to share information, connect with others who "get it," and voice and troubleshoot all kinds of accessibility concerns—from crowdsourcing practitioner recommendations to ideas for a good date restaurant that could accommodate both gluten-free diets and wheelchair users.

In my years of being in community with sick folks, I have found that many with chronic illness don't choose to identify as disabled, or don't know that it is even an option. Unfortunately, ableism is rampant in many chronic illness support groups where being sick and disabled is generally considered bad, undesirable, and something that needs to be fixed. But when folks with chronic illness join disabled communities and learn about disability justice, we can experience a whole new sense of belonging and empowerment.

What a lot of spoonies don't realize is that chronic illness is considered a disability under the Americans with Disabilities Act (ADA), meaning that both employers and businesses are legally obligated to provide you with "reasonable accommodations." Unfortunately, that doesn't mean they will, but as more of us claim the disabled identity, own it and demand equity, we grow our collective power to change the status quo for ourselves and others.

Choosing to identify as disabled and work in community with other disabled folks provides a way for our overlapping communities to come together and ask for what we need with a bigger, broader voice. And the accommodations required by sick and disabled people to participate fully in society are not so different from broader societal needs. Our communities just need them more often and more urgently. By lifting up the needs of sick and disabled individuals, we are providing more options and accessibility for everyone.

Years ago when I couldn't stand up for long periods of time, I asked a local music venue if they could reserve a seat for me for a particular show. I love live music, but I mostly stopped going to shows when my legs started feeling weak all the time. That one venue was happy to reserve a chair for me and did so many other times. Other venues didn't make it as easy, but I'm sure if I had gotten a group of people together to push them on it, we could have effectively pushed all venues in the area to do the same.

This would benefit people with short-term injuries, seniors, and all kinds of people who don't usually identify as disabled. Given that more than half of Americans have a chronic health condition, we can assume that most people have needs that they might not even know could be accommodated in many public spaces. If they could acknowledge and receive these accommodations, they might be able to do more and move through the world with much greater ease.

I personally began identifying as disabled fairly recently on the suggestion of a student activist at Harvard Kennedy School, where I used to work. I considered myself intermittently disabled because at the time I was generally feeling well outside of occasional flare-ups. I understand now that claiming the disabled identity wholeheartedly is more useful in the context of collective action.

Even if I am not in fact disabled every day, it doesn't mean I am not disabled. There have been a lot of times in my healing journey when I have been very clearly and consistently disabled. I was speaking to my family about getting a wheelchair at one point because I couldn't stand, and I was sick of not being able to go anywhere that required standing. Still, for years, it didn't occur to me to identify as disabled. But through connecting with more disabled individuals, I realized both that I am disabled and that disabled folks are my people.

I've felt so validated by my disabled buddies and have learned so much from them about how to advocate for personal and collective wellbeing in many contexts. Disabled folks who have been disabled for a while, sometimes their whole lives, are often experts in surviving within systems that are not designed for them, from the workplace to the doctor's office.

A lot of stuff that I struggled with early on—feeling like a burden, navigating insurance and health care bureaucracy, not knowing how to get support in the workplace—most of my disabled buddies learned how to navigate with grace years before me. Issues that people just complained about in chronic illness support groups, my disabled buddies had found solutions to.

They are also experts on what support is available through the state and other institutions. When able-bodied individuals get injured and/or become ill, they are usually confronted for the first time with the discomfort, bureaucracy, and injustice that disabled Americans navigate on a daily basis.

Disabled folks have also opened my eyes to just how rampant ableism is, and how deeply we have all internalized it. Getting support to see where ableism lives in you is a crucial component of healing. The more disabled buddies you have, the more you can support each other to see that some of your struggles are really rooted in internalized ableism, therefore freeing you up to live your life more fully on your terms.

Identifying as disabled may not be a fit for everyone but I encourage you to explore it if you have not already. Sick and disabled folks still experience a lot of discrimination, so coming out publicly as disabled is worth thoughtful consideration. Even employers and businesses who want to do the right thing aren't hip to what it really means to be inclusive and accessible. Choosing who to tell and when, especially in hiring processes, may be different in different industries and contexts, so I recommend doing your research. Identifying as disabled on a job application will get you on the top of the pile with the federal government for example, but it might mean you don't get an interview with a local business. In some contexts, you may be required to get disability benefits and/or recognition from your state of residence in order to take advantage of certain resources. Outside of navigating the government and work realms, you might find that identifying as disabled socially, or even just privately, has its own benefits. Choosing to be in relationship with disabled folks can sweeten and broaden your community, help you feel seen, give you a new framework for political activism, and support in learning your rights as someone with a body that doesn't move through this ableist capitalist reality with the same ease as other bodies.

The more we build disabled community and come together to make our communities more accessible now, the more rapidly we can arrive in a future where the focus of our attention is on matters beyond access and inclusion. I want to invite you to imagine that for a moment. If you and your sick and disabled kin didn't have to spend so many spoons thinking about how to get places or wondering if your needs would be accommodated in those places, for example, what might be possible? What might you do with those extra spoons? What other social challenges could we heal and transform together if we already had what we needed?

Here are some disability resources that might be supportive:
- **Sins Invalid's disability justice primer *Skin, Tooth, and Bone: The Basis of Movement is Our People*,** is a great intro

to disability justice and how to apply it in organizations, planning events, and other social movement work.

- *Care Work: Dreaming Disability Justice* by Leah Lakshmi Piepzna-Samarsinha is a beautiful entrance into the history of disability justice, creating care webs, centering healing justice in our movements, and uplifting sick and disabled, queer, trans BIPOC brilliance.
- **How to Get On** howtogeton.wordpress.com/ Provides guides on applying for Social Security and Medicaid, finding affordable housing, how to get a wheelchair, how to get a home care aid, and so much more. It's also bright and cheery and has a very loving vibe. It might be particularly helpful for folks with ME and other homebound and bed bound individuals.
- **Job Accommodation Network (JAN)** https://askjan.org/ is a phenomenal resource for all things related to disability and work, for individuals and employers. Among other things, it has a 1-800 number you can call for free consults, and links to several job databases specifically for folks with disabilities.
- **Chronically Capable** https://www.wearecapable.org/ is a platform that connects chronically ill folks with remote work opportunities with supportive employers. It's less robust than JAN, but growing all the time.
- **Disability Visibility Project** https://disabilityvisibilityproject.com/ is a project of disability justice advocate Alice Wong that encompasses a blog, podcast, an advice column, and much more.
- **Life In My Days** https://www.lifeinmydays.com/ is a peer- & youth-led international non-profit supporting communities and individuals on their journeys for self-actualization. I attended an awesome training on disability justice led by this

group and they have a lot of solid content on their website about living with disabilities.

- **CripNews** https://cripnews.substack.com/ is a wonderful weekly newsletter about disability art and politics put together by Kevin Gotkin.

Reflection Questions:
- What did you notice reading this section? What feelings arose for you?
- If you do not already, how does it feel to consider identifying as disabled? Do you feel fear? Freedom? A mix of emotions?
- Do you see a small sweet next step you want to take to learn about disability benefits, disability community, or disability justice?

Strengthen Your Intuition

"The body knows things about which the mind is ignorant."
—Jacques Lecoq

*"Don't try to comprehend with your mind. Your minds are
very limited. Use your intuition."*
—Madeleine L'Engle, *A Wind in the Door*

So far, we've talked about how seeking more connection, training your
brain, and finding new ways to talk about your health challenges can
support your healing. Now I'm going to talk about how to hone and
call upon your intuition as a primary healing strategy. I'll explain how
consulting your intuition regularly can make your healing journey
easier by helping you save energy and get crystal clear on what you
need to be doing. I'll share examples of how consulting my intuition
has supported my healing, suggest intuitive practices that can support
your healing, and offer resources to help you strengthen your intuitive
abilities in general.

A natural reaction to becoming ill or experiencing pain is to try to
fix what's wrong. While it sounds counterintuitive, we actually have to
surrender to what is before we can find our way through it. So many
of us get obsessed with finding the right doctor, the right medicine,
the right diagnosis. Sometimes we don't even give something time to
work before we jump to the next thing. I call this "the chase." The
chase keeps us externally focused, meaning we're always looking for
answers outside of ourselves. It is energy intensive, exhausting, and
rarely produces results on its own.

Living with the mindset that your health is at the hands of other people is disempowering AF and can leave you feeling totally hopeless when you don't find the support you're looking for. If you've been living with health challenges for a while, I bet you've experienced at least a little of this. I've seen myself and my clients go through cycles where we do a lot of chasing, don't get the results we're looking for, and we give up for a while until things get really bad again.

Then we become determined to find THE thing that will give us relief from our anguish. It's kind of the worst, especially because there is no *one* thing that will heal you—and the answers to what *will* support you actually lie within. The healing path is as much if not more internal than it is external. That is, it's great to have professionals that can help you on your path, and I do recommend seeking that support, but ultimately *you* still have to steer the ship and confront any internal blocks or demons that are limiting your healing.

Most of us know intuitively that perpetually seeking answers outside ourselves isn't helpful. Most of us also understand that there is information inside of us, but we avoid it because we suspect it will be uncomfortable. Since we're already physically uncomfortable, it feels easier to resist additional discomfort.

In this way, looking outward for answers becomes a convenient, unconscious distraction from inward things we're avoiding. It's so normal, but it's a pattern worth disrupting. You actually have inside of you the capacity to find the help you need and heal your way through whatever you're experiencing right now. This innate healing ability is something we are all born with.

I want to invite you to put the book down for a moment and take a few deep breaths. When you look and see, do you see/feel that you have the power to achieve what you want, in healing and in your life in general?

If not yet, it's okay. It will come.

If you do see/feel it, what does it feel like in your body to acknowledge that you have agency in your healing?

Your intuition is one of your most powerful healing tools. All of us are born with a strong intuition. If you've spent any time with kids, you know this to be true. They're incredibly intuitive. Unfortunately, our society and our public education system emphasize thinking over feeling, so over time most of us lose touch with our intuition.

Then, when we leave school and start facing big decisions and challenges, we try to use our critical thinking skills to reason our way to the answer, rather than taking the time to ask ourselves, "What is true for me? What do I really want?" We forget about our intuition and when we do get a feeling about something, it can be hard to trust it, especially if the feeling conflicts with what the analytical mind has to say, or what we've been told to believe. When we aren't present to our intuition, we spend a lot of time overthinking and questioning everything. It's exhausting, as you might know from experience.

That's not to say that critical thinking isn't helpful—it is!—but it's only one of the tools at our disposal. Trying to go through life with critical thinking as your only tool for making life decisions is like trying to slice a watermelon with a paring knife. It's infuriating and dangerous. Having a chef's knife makes the whole experience much easier and more fun. Your intuition is like that chef's knife, and it needs to be sharp to be useful. You might need to practice using your intuition regularly in order to hone it and build trust in it.

So what the heck *is* intuition?

Another way to think about it is the unconscious mind. Most scientists agree that 95-98% of the decisions we make every day are made in the unconscious mind, meaning we only spend 2-5% of our time on any given day making conscious decisions. The rest of the time we're acting on instincts. So, if the unconscious mind is what's really running the show for us, does it make sense for us to leave the conscious mind in charge of important decisions about our health and wellbeing? Probably not.

A slightly more spiritual take is that when you consult your intuition, you are consulting a well of knowledge that is much bigger than you and contains the wisdom of your ancestors, the Earth, the divine, and the entire living human collective. When using your intuition you are consulting the wisdom in all the cells of your being rather than just the ones in your brain.

Even though my clients now know me as a proselytizer for intuition-development as a healing tool, I mistrusted my own intuition for years, and sometimes I still dismiss it. I'll see myself doing something, like carrying too many things, and I think, "That's not a good idea," and then I do it anyway and spill rice all over the floor. That's a small example, but humans do this in bigger ways all the time.

We take jobs that deep down we know we won't like, and we date people when we intuitively know they're not a good fit. And when things don't work out, we usually make up some story that places the blame on someone or something else. Conversely, when we make a choice to do something based on intuition and get great results, we call it luck.

A life coach once explained to me that the right side of your body is your masculine side and is concerned with critical thinking, while your left side is your feminine and more intuitive side. This set off a light bulb for me. Going back to 2004, all my chronic pain has been on the right side of my body.

No doctor, herbalist, chiropractor, or body worker has been able to explain why it is so one-sided. It occurred to me while talking to this coach that my pain could be the result of years of ignoring my intuition. I then decided to start exploring honoring my intuition as a possible remedy to the pain. I began to regularly ask myself questions, starting with small things that didn't feel like a big deal. At the grocery store, I'd put my hand on a certain bag of chips or piece of fruit and ask myself silently, "will my body like this?" I've had a lot of food sensitivities, and my body is changing all the time, so eating the "right" things can be tricky. Interestingly, when I would ask about the food items, I always got a clear "yes" or "no."

When I ignored my intuition and ate things that got a clear "no," I got a stomachache every time. When I lost my car key at the grocery store once and couldn't find it anywhere in the store or the parking lot, I asked myself, "Where is my key?" I got a clear "in the car." I didn't believe that because when I shined light in the car, I couldn't see a key anywhere. I also mistakenly thought that my fairly new car was smart enough to prevent me from locking myself out. If only! Two hours later, when I got into the car with a spare, I found my key wedged between the seat and the center console, just out of sight. It was in fact in the car as my intuition told me.

These are just small things, but learning to ask and trust your intuition can be useful on a much broader and deeper level. It can help you make big decisions with more ease and confidence, perform better in your work, and take a break from the chase without putting your healing on hold.

When I first wrote this section, I'd been trying, with mixed results, to heal what was diagnosed as small intestinal bacterial overgrowth (SIBO) and a deteriorated stomach lining. Sometimes my gut didn't bother me, sometimes it hurt, sometimes I was super bloated. It was not the worst thing in the world, but it was not the easiest either. During one month of the SIBO saga, I was both in a lot of pain and really depressed. Like, struggled to make myself do *anything* depressed. I had just spent four days trying to do the Specific Carbohydrate Diet (SCD) intro diet, which looked like two days of sticking to it perfectly, followed by two days of eating the prescribed diet *and* binge eating potato chips.

I was exhausted, feeling lost about what to do next, and waiting to hear back from a naturopath about my best next steps. Then I remembered that I could just ask my body! I laid on the couch, took a minute to arrange pillows so I was super comfortable, placed my hands on my belly (skin to skin), and closed my eyes. I took deep breaths for several minutes, bringing my attention down into my belly. Then I asked, "What do you need?" The answer I got was "a break." I kept inquiring.

"A break from what?"

"Solid food."

"What would you like instead?"

"Juice. Soup."

"How long?"

"Three days."

Feeling like the instructions were clear, I started the next day. I was surprised by how much easier it was to stick to this intuition-prescribed diet since it had come from within me, and not from some outside force. And in the first day and a half when I experienced a near constant headache, I didn't worry about it. I didn't try to fix it. I just understood it was part of the process.

Interestingly, in the first two days of this cleanse, a hawk flew across my path each day as I was out walking in the neighborhood. Hawks are understood by many cultures to be symbols of broadening intuition and even psychic awareness. On day three, I woke up feeling pretty out of it, so I consulted my belly again, "Would it be okay to eat some solid food?" I got a strong "yes" and confirmation on which foods to start with. After I ate, I felt like a million bucks, like a whole new person, and so excited to be alive. After days of wanting to talk to no one, I went to a brunch with my partner's theatre colleagues and schmoozed like a champ, loving every minute of it.

One of the most common struggles I hear from folks with health challenges, and particularly from my Lyme family, is the challenge of never knowing what to do next. When health goes south or another promising medicine doesn't help, there's this painful big familiar question mark that keeps coming back. Naturally, folks try to problem solve. And because our mind doesn't have the answer, we exhaust ourselves researching and trying to decide between different options that may or may not provide any relief or healing because there is no clear cure.

What I've found in my journey and in my work with clients is that our body has the answers we're looking for. And part of my mission on Earth is to help folks experience less suffering by turning to their intuition instead of Google. The body knows so many things that the mind doesn't. The body also knows things *before* the mind. This is why our instincts can save us from an oncoming car before our cognitive mind can tell us to move.

The more we can give the mind a rest and tap into the wisdom of our bodies, the easier healing becomes. Since we're doing exactly what the body wants and needs and are not subjecting it to a bunch of products and experiences that it doesn't, we get better results. Acting from intuition also saves energy because we're not riding the emotional see-saw of "Should I do this? Should I do that? Will this even work?" If you cultivate your intuition, you can get easy, clear answers to those questions.

I usually loathe sports analogies, but I like the way that Timothy Gallwey describes the power of intuition in *The Inner Game of Tennis.* The best tennis, he writes, is played from the unconscious mind. He divides the self into two parts, Self 1 and Self 2. Self 1 is the conscious, thinking mind and Self 2 is the unconscious, intuitive mind, where the natural talent lies. While training tennis players, Gallwey noticed that his students were way more successful when they were playing from Self 2. When he'd say, "Hold your racket like this, and put your feet like this," they started *thinking* about what to do and didn't play as well. When he had them simply watch him hit 10 balls in a row and then asked them to imitate him, without instruction, their form drastically improved. I take the lesson to be that when we think less, and feel more, we get better results.

My suggestion is that you take a break from the chase. I'm not saying don't go to the doctor but give yourself some time to look inward instead of outward. You can ask yourself what amount of time feels right, whether it's two weeks, three months, or longer. In that time, consult your body for answers and let yourself do things that fill you up and nourish you. Notice if that changes your experience.

If you're having trouble breathing, for example, and you don't know why, ask your lungs what the deal is. Start by taking some time to get centered, either by meditating, doing some gentle movement, or both (see suggestions in Affirmations, Breathwork, and Yoga Practices). Then lovingly lay your hands on your chest, over your lungs and ask what they want. You might say, "Lungs, I love you and I want you to feel good. What do you need?" Then observe what comes up for you.

It could be images, words, a message, a color. If you're not sure how to interpret what comes up, start by writing about it. That usually turns up some nuggets of information and even if it doesn't, you can revisit it later. You can also share the info with an intuitive friend, mentor, or spiritual teacher, and ask for their take on it.

Remember that their take isn't necessarily the truth but may help you see *your* truth. You can also ask for guidance in your dreams if you're someone who remembers your dreams. Even if you're not, sometimes just giving yourself some space and time to sit with and consider any information you've received will allow you to come back and interpret it with more ease. It's a practice, and I find it's useful to think of your intuition like a muscle. The more you use it, the stronger it gets.

When you're in the moment of having a flare or acute episode of any kind, it can be hard to remember that you actually have the answers and that your body can guide the way. This is another reason to practice regularly consulting your intuition, no matter how you're feeling.

It's good to create some kind of visual reminder for yourself in the form of a sticky note, a note on your phone, or a calendar alert that says something like, "Use your intuition for the win!" I once got a fortune in a fortune cookie that simply read, "Trust your intuition today," and I've been transferring it from the front cover of one daily planner to another for years, protected under layers of Scotch tape.

As you start to build a relationship with your intuition, it's great to ask yourself questions with verifiable answers. If you ask your intuition a question and you're not sure if you're getting an answer, just make it up. You might hear some mind chatter about how you're just guessing, or pretending. That's totally fine and doesn't make you wrong. Take note of when you "guess" correctly. This will give you more evidence that your intuition is strong and that you can trust it.

Here are some easy exercises to start with:
- On your way to get the mail, guess how many pieces of mail you have.
- At the grocery store, look in your cart/basket and guess how much the total will be before you checkout.
- If a bus stops in front of you, predict how many people will get off.
- When you get up in the morning, guess how many calls or texts you'll get in the day and write it down.
- Predict the weather.

Then compare notes! You might be surprised at how often you're close or correct. And the more you get clear, correct answers, the more it will build your confidence for bigger questions like, "Should I work with this doctor? Is this treatment going to be supportive? Should I take this job?" Also take note of any intuitive hits you get, like knowing someone is going to call you right before they do, or getting the feeling that you should drive one way instead of another way right before seeing a blocked road.

If you're consulting your intuition regularly but not getting clear answers about your health, or you're unsure how to interpret your answers, it can be a good time to call in support. This is part of my work as a coach and an intuitive mentor, and there are plenty of healers and practitioners out there who work with intuition.

I got into intuition via the work of Lyme survivor, author, homeopath, and medical intuitive Katina Makris and have learned more from Ellen Tadd, Sonia Choquette, my friend Heather Smith, and others along the way. I like using the chakras[83] as a guide (more on those in the next section) as Makris and Tadd do, but different teachers and healers have all kinds of tools and methods.

At one point I took an animal communication class and found that a lot of the same skills I'd developed to interpret what my body wanted I could also use to understand what animals were trying to tell me. One of the best resources I've found on intuitive development is Sonia Choquette's book *The Psychic Pathway: A Workbook for Reawakening the Voice of Your Soul.*

It's an easy read, good for beginners, and it is full of awesome exercises to help you cultivate and trust your intuition. Choquette includes a guide to using tarot cards, oracles cards, runes, and the I Ching, and there are tons of resources online if you want to play with those modalities as a vehicle for accessing intuition. I've enjoyed using Biddy Tarot and TheTarotGuide.com to learn tarot card meanings and I sometimes consult tarot to help myself understand what I'm feeling or what's happening around me.

I also use shamanic journeying in my own practice and find it to be a great tool for getting clarity in decision-making. If that is something

---

83 Chakras are energy centers in the body as outlined by early Hindu traditions. "Early Sanskrit texts speak of them both as meditative visualizations combining flowers and mantras and as physical entities in the body." https://en.wikipedia.org/wiki/Chakra Accessed 10/5/2020.

you want to explore, look for a local shaman who can mentor you or take an online class to learn the basics.

Remember that you don't have to be a professional intuitive or psychic to get life-changing results from consulting your intuition. Just make a point of consulting your intuition regularly and see what you find. The more you use it, the stronger it gets. As you work with it, you might find that your psychic abilities grow, and you know what people are going to say before they say it, or you know that something is going to happen before it does.

This is normal and nothing to be afraid of. I think we're all a little psychic and when we make room for our abilities to grow, all kinds of gifts can be revealed. Again, if it ever wigs you out, seek support. Maybe talk to your ancestors about it. You can ask your intuition where to look for guides and teachers. What I keep seeing in my own life, and the lives of my clients, is that the more we consult our intuition, the easier life becomes. So much struggle just melts away. This is because our intuition can show us what we need to live in alignment and practice coherence. It's pretty much the best!

Exercise & Reflection:

Choose one of the exercises mentioned in this section and try it out for three days in a row. Record the results in your healing journal and reflect on the following:
- What are you noticing about your intuition?
- How often are you correct?
- How and when might you consult your intuition when making decisions related to your healing?

Explore the Metaphysical

Every ailment and dis-ease has a physical and a metaphysical component. My working definition of metaphysical is all that we cannot see, feel, or touch. In many cases—and some would say all cases—the root cause of a physical illness is emotional, spiritual, or mental, or a little bit of all three. Metaphysical components of physical health challenges might include repressed emotions, trauma, stress, ancestral trauma, past-life experiences, or spiritual disconnection, to name a few.

This is part of why cultivating your intuition is so important. It's one of the best tools we have for identifying and healing the metaphysical causes of illness. The degree to which a certain ailment's causes are physical vs. metaphysical can vary. Doctors, mystical healers, and everyone in between have a million different opinions about what really causes dis-ease in the body.

From the shamanic perspective, for example, illness is the result of becoming separated from part of your soul and can be remedied via soul retrieval. I won't discuss that here, but if that sparks something in you, you might enjoy reading Sandra Ingerman's *Soul Retrieval: Mending the Fragmented Self* or enlisting the support of a shaman, which you might be able to do online.

If you've done a lot of work to heal your physical body and you're not seeing results, that could indicate a metaphysical component that hasn't been addressed. If you feel caught in a pattern of getting better and then relapsing or acquiring another health challenge after healing a previous one, chances are there's a metaphysical block that hasn't been fully addressed yet.

Let's say for example that someone has an auto-immune disease and also has low self-worth because they grew up with an abusive parent. As long as the self-worth piece is not addressed, it will be very difficult for the person to heal. They probably have some internal gunk that is blocking them from feeling worthy of healing, support, and/ or nurturing, but not knowing how to get it. They might not even be aware of this block and how it is affecting their actions and the way they show up to their own healing.

It's widely understood that our thoughts shape our reality, and people will often come to me saying that they need an attitude adjustment to get them reinvested in their healing. Of course, changing your attitude and mindset is valuable, and that's a big part of what I help people with as a coach. But there are also usually some underlying psychic wounds or trauma that need to be addressed in order for someone to be successful in their healing.

Physical interventions and attitude adjustments are not enough. I said a lot about the connection between trauma and illness in Section 2, so here I want to look more specifically at *how* to work with trauma and maybe even heal it. I will offer some approaches that have supported me, and at the end of the chapter, I include a list of modalities and resources that might be supportive for you on your journey.

As a reminder, when I mention trauma in this context, what I'm talking about is dysregulation in the nervous system as the result of a traumatic event, events, or repeated violence, abuse, or neglect that have not been metabolized.

In *Radical Dharma: Talking Race, Love, and Liberation,* Lama Rod Owens defines trauma and its healability as such:[84]:

> The creation of a context that does not privilege my deepest desire to return home and inhabit my own agency and body, but instead triggers disembodiment and a loss of awareness of the body and its experiences. Thus, trauma becomes a cyclical

---

84 Rev. angel Kyodo Williams, Jasmine Syedullah, and Lama Rod Owens, Radical Dharma: Talking Race, Love, and Liberation (North Atlantic Books, 2016).

experience of continuous unfolding, of continuous movement through places without consent as it perpetuates terror, despair, hopelessness, and disconnection.

He also writes:

When I speak of trauma, I speak of experiences that impact how we relate to ourselves and to others around us. These experiences, mostly related to our emotional capacities and also called woundedness, hurting, aching, or pain, refer both to the subtle and gross experiences that make it very difficult to feel confident, safe, or to experience happiness, wellbeing, and balance. In this understanding of trauma, trauma can be healed. Through the cultivation of awareness practice, we can learn to identify our traumas, accept them, investigate them, and learn to let them go…

It can be useful to understand that the trauma impacting your health could be from something that's happened in your life, it could be your ancestors' trauma, or you could even be feeling the trauma of a past life. In Section 2, I mentioned the concept of intergenerational trauma, which I've heard shamanic healers describe as "ancestral burden" or "legacy burden."

The idea is that you could be carrying and suffering from the trauma inflicted on your ancestors. In my journey, I've realized that a lot of what I'm healing is actually my grandmother's trauma from living through World War II as a teenager in Belgium. Some healers believe that physical and mental illness can stem from past life trauma or karma. There are scientists, namely at the University of Virginia, who have been studying children's claims of reincarnation for decades, so we may not be too far from confirming this scientifically.[85]

I've had multiple energy healers explain that my recurring right-side pain is some kind of past-life issue. One healer, while doing energy work with me, said she saw me as a monk in a past life, suffering alone in a cave with an infection in my right side. Parts of what she described felt very resonant. So far, this understanding hasn't shifted the pain very much, but I'm willing to stay open!

Regardless of where it stems from, we all carry a certain amount of traumatic stress in our nervous systems. We need to heal this in order to heal chronic health challenges, in part by bringing repressed feelings to light and moving them up and out of our bodies. In his book *My Grandmother's Hands*, somatic therapist Resmaa Menakem calls this "metabolizing" trauma in the body. Re-evaluation Counseling, a form of peer counseling, encourages revisiting "early hurts" from adolescence and "discharging" the emotions that were not processed at the time the painful experience occurred.[86]

What these approaches argue is that some of the keys to your healing exist under a pile of repressed feelings. Once you create space to feel and move those feelings, you may experience a sense of freedom in your body that was previously unimaginable. That's certainly been my experience.

When I was operating under the assumption that I had fibromyalgia, before I got diagnosed with Lyme, I read that there was a connection between fibro and trauma, and that healing one's trauma could reduce pain dramatically. After I got a Lyme diagnosis, I found that most folks with chronic Lyme are also trauma survivors. In talking to one of my practitioners about trauma, I shared that I felt like an outlier because I didn't have a significant trauma history. He looked me in the eye and asked, "What makes trauma 'significant?'"

As he helped me understand, trauma is trauma, and being chronically ill is in itself traumatic. Up until that point, I had assumed that because I had so much privilege and hadn't endured something akin

---

86 Menakem, My Grandmother's Hands: Racialized Trauma and the Pathway to Mending Our Hearts and Bodies.

to the worst incidents of abuse I had ever read about, I hadn't experienced trauma. I have a different understanding today, and I have made a point of exploring and welcoming my own trauma history. I actually came into this life in a pretty dramatic and traumatic way. In a different time, both my mother and I probably would have died. I was a breech baby, meaning I was in the womb upside down, feet first.

I flipped at the last minute, getting my umbilical cord wrapped around my neck, and was extracted via emergency C-section. My mother's epidural hadn't kicked in yet when the doctor started surgery and she could feel him cutting her open. Perhaps unsurprisingly, I was a terrible sleeper in my first year of life. I've also experienced sexual assault, and very likely have some ancestral burden from both sides of the family. And that's all layered on top of traumas I've acquired simply from living in America in this time. Seeing and honoring that I do in fact have trauma to heal has helped me tremendously in my healing journey.

Luckily for those of us on the healing path, there are many modalities for healing trauma. For a lot of folks, therapy can be a nice place to start, especially if you have health insurance that covers it. There are many different kinds of therapy, so it is important to find a therapist whose experience, cultural literacy, and demeanor are a good fit for you. That said, talk therapy can miss really deep stuff—things that we aren't even conscious of, that we might not have words for—so additional healing modalities may be supportive.

Therapy is also traditionally aligned with allopathic medicine. It isn't always culturally sensitive or inclusive of trans people, disabled people, and folks of other marginalized identities. That said, there are therapists of all identities, and some bring other tools into their practice to provide a more holistic therapeutic experience.

For example, some practitioners bill insurance for therapy, but actually do shamanic work. It's worth doing your research and asking people you trust for recommendations. That said, if talking about stuff sounds like the worst, or you just want something different, a body-focused modality like yoga therapy or Somatic Experiencing may feel like a better fit. There are therapists who work with these modalities and take insurance and/or charge on a sliding scale.

Next, I'll share three frameworks that you can use on your own to identify potential metaphysical sources of illness: Louise Hay's approach, the Chakra system, and the Chinese Medicine Body Clock. These frameworks may not help you identify trauma specifically, but they can help you see patterns, behaviors, grief, energetic blocks, or beliefs that are the result of trauma and are having an effect on your healing. At the end of this chapter, I also provide a list of trauma healing modalities that have been supportive for me and/or my clients. I invite you to consult your intuition about whether anything I share feels worth pursuing for you.

Though I don't wholeheartedly endorse metaphysical healer Louise Hay's work, the list of symptoms and metaphysical associations listed in her book, *You Can Heal Your Life* can be illuminating, or at least an interesting starting place when looking for the metaphysical underpinnings of a particular condition. The knees, for example, according to Hay, are associated with pride and ego. Knee problems could indicate a stubborn ego, an unwillingness to bend, fear, and inflexibility.

If you don't have access to the book, you can Google "Louise Hay Symptom List," and see if it feels useful to you. When I have a new symptom, I like to look it up in Hay's symptom list and see if the description resonates. Often it does. Sometimes I don't see the connection until much later, or I need help from others to see it clearly. Occasionally I don't see any connection, but that doesn't mean it's not there. I can already hear some of you saying, "my knees hurt because Lyme spirochetes are eating all the soft tissue in my joints!"

Yes, and are you open to looking at possible metaphysical causes that could be exacerbating or perpetuating the underlying bacterial infection? If you're totally new to the metaphysical aspects of illness and pain, you may experience a lot of resistance to exploring illness from this perspective. That's normal. Come back to it a few times and see if you can be open to new insights.

You might also explore your symptoms through the lens of the chakras. Hinduism, Buddhism, and Jainism understand the chakras as energy centers in the body. Energy in this case is electricity. Our cells conduct electrical currents, and electricity is how the nervous system sends signals between the brain and the rest of the body. The seven main chakras run along the spine, from the base to the top of the head, and each chakra aligns with a plexus of nerves and a major endocrine gland.

The endocrine system sends out hormones that regulate important bodily functions like sleep, metabolism, reproduction, mood, sexual function, and reproduction. When energy is blocked in one of the chakras, it can impact the function of the corresponding gland. Similarly, the nerve plexuses in the chakras are connected to certain organs, so when a certain chakra is blocked, it can affect the electrical communication to the corresponding organ, causing disease. Chakras become blocked or congested because of emotional repression, substance abuse, negative energy, oppression, and trauma. They can be balanced or unblocked through meditation, yoga, energy work, and other practices.

I am still learning about this "subtle body" or "energy-body" myself—there's so much out there—but I have learned a lot about myself and what my body needs simply by tuning into the chakras or energy centers in my own body. For example, I've had chronic right sacroiliac pain for years. It started after an injury, so I know the initial cause, but I've had a hell of a time healing it.

When the pain was particularly bad one spring, one of my mentors suggested that I read about the second chakra, which is located near the hips, and associated with sexuality, desire, creativity, relationships, pleasure, and procreation. In reading about it I learned that hip pain can result from an inability to love yourself. As I upped my self-love game in the last few years and continued to get regular chiropractic adjustments, I noticed a huge improvement. Not only is the pain from the injured area greatly reduced, but my hips and lower back are much more open than they've ever been. One day I realized that I could get into some yoga poses more deeply than I ever had before. For the yoga-literate: it was easier to touch the floor in forward fold, my hips touched my heels in child's pose, I could squat for the first time ever with my hips lower than my knees, and I no longer needed props in pigeon pose because both hips sat snuggly on the ground. It was pretty wild.

I love that the chakras can be used like this, as a diagnostic tool for uncovering the metaphysical components of a physical condition. To give another example, if you are having trouble sleeping, it could be related to a seventh chakra issue. The seventh chakra is associated with presence, higher consciousness, and liberation from limiting patterns, among other things. So if you're having trouble sleeping, you might find that joining a meditation group helps.

Here is a rough hand drawn chart of the chakras and some of their physical and metaphysical associations, starting with the first at the base of the body. What is listed here is just scratching the surface of what is known about the chakras so if this resonates with you, I recommend doing more of your own research on each of them. When you look at the chart, what do you notice? What stands out to you?

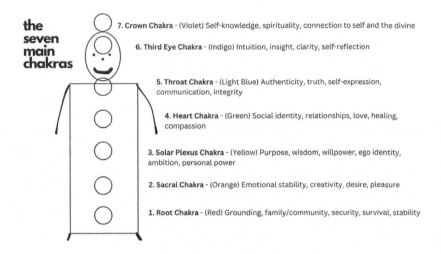

the seven main chakras

7. Crown Chakra - (Violet) Self-knowledge, spirituality, connection to self and the divine

6. Third Eye Chakra - (Indigo) Intuition, insight, clarity, self-reflection

5. Throat Chakra - (Light Blue) Authenticity, truth, self-expression, communication, integrity

4. Heart Chakra - (Green) Social identity, relationships, love, healing, compassion

3. Solar Plexus Chakra - (Yellow) Purpose, wisdom, willpower, ego identity, ambition, personal power

2. Sacral Chakra - (Orange) Emotional stability, creativity, desire, pleasure

1. Root Chakra - (Red) Grounding, family/community, security, survival, stability

If the metaphysical associations of one of the chakras resonate with you, try putting a hand on that spot and asking what it wants to tell you. For example, for the fifth chakra you'd place a hand, or even just your mind's eye, on the base of your throat. This is a good practice to do when you're more relaxed, like after meditating or taking a bath. I learned this approach from Katina Makris and I have used it a lot in my own healing and with my clients. It can be a great way to get information about yourself that is hard to access in other ways in your everyday life.

In addition to the chakras, I have used the Chinese Medicine Body Clock as a way to identify metaphysical funks. A few years ago, I started experiencing intermittent one-sided pain in the middle of my back after I ate. I did my due diligence and got an ultrasound to rule out gallstones. I didn't have any stones and everything looked normal. I saw a gastroenterologist who said it could be an acid issue or nerve pain.

To explore the acid issue, I started taking hydrochloric acid and it did go away for a little while, and then it came back. Around the same time, I also began waking up every morning between 4-5am. One of my practitioners said something about waking up at "lung time." I didn't get a chance to ask what she meant so I set out to explore that further.

In Traditional Chinese Medicine (TCM), consistent late night/early morning waking times (and midday sleepiness) are associated with different meridians, or energy channels in the body. Each meridian is paired with an organ and an element – earth, water, metal, wood, and fire – and each element is associated with certain emotions. The 4-5am slot corresponds with metal, which rules the lung and large intestine and is associated with grief and loss (the negative emotion) and courage (the positive emotion).

When I saw that, my first reaction was frustration, "I haven't had any big losses. There's nothing to grieve!" My herbalist and others have told me that the right-side headaches I've had for years are associated with anger and my initial reaction to that was similar, "My life is pretty great. What is there to be angry about?" But, since I was sick of my back hurting every single time I ate, no matter what I ate, and even sometimes when I didn't eat, I decided to give myself some space to ask these questions and listen to the answers. I sat down on my back porch with some herbal tea one morning and wrote down the words "grief and loss." Then I wrote the questions, "What might I be grieving? What have I lost?" And I started writing.

It turned out to be a long, emotional list. I had a good long cry about it and it was a very cathartic experience. My back hurt less afterwards, I slept through the night that evening, and stopped waking at 4 am altogether. The same back pain has come up again at other times and I have been able to reduce the pain the same way, by bringing attention to the underlying emotions and giving them space to move.

For copyright reasons I cannot include my favorite version of the TCM Body Clock but I recommend looking up Jane Barthelemy's "Chinese Medicine 24-Hour Circadian Clock" online, which can be found at https://www.lixinacupuncture.com/blog/2017/8/3/tcm-body-clock.[87]

87 Lixin Zhang, "TCM Body Clock," Lixin Acupuncture Clinics® Denver (Lixin Acupuncture Clinics® Denver, August 3, 2017), https://www.lixinacupuncture.com/blog/2017/8/3/tcm-body-clock

So, in addition to cultivating your own intuition, and regularly asking your body what it's trying to tell you, you have a wide swath of metaphysical diagnostic tools at your disposal. Louise Hay's list, the chakra system, and the TCM body clock are just a few examples of what's out there. Many people have written volumes about the systems that exist and I encourage you to read about them, take workshops on them, or work with practitioners who have devoted their lives to using and understanding these incredible healing systems.

If you're thinking, "That sounds nice, you hippy, but it's not for me," I hear you. I would have said the same thing earlier in my healing journey. And, if all you've ever known is science-based medicine, this may sound very foreign and quacky. Just know that we have a lot of wisdom in our bodies and there are many ways to access it. Accessing that wisdom may feel unfamiliar, uncomfortable, and maybe even confusing at first, but it's ever-so-fruitful. Most of my clients are amazed at how much information they get even the first time they use these systems.

Modalities for Healing Trauma and Other Metaphysical Burdens:

This is not an exhaustive list, because that could be its own book, but my hope is that this will give you at least a few things to explore.
- Somatic Experiencing was developed by Peter Levine and was created to help people heal from PTSD and other trauma-related health and mental health challenges by focusing on the patient's physical sensations. It involves the client tracking their own felt experience. Practitioners are usually therapists but other kinds of practitioners can be certified as well. https://traumahealing.org/ [88]

---

[88] There are many kinds of somatic therapy and you might also benefit from Googling "Somatic therapist near me," or "Somatic coach near me." If you have health insurance it might cover a somatic therapist and/or therapists who practice some of the modalities above. There are even therapists who also work as shamans.

- Core Energetics is also concerned with bringing consciousness to where trauma lives in the body. It involves freeing up
energy blocks in the body through physical manipulation,
exercises, and breathing techniques. https://traumahealing.
org/
- Expressive Arts Therapy, which can include art therapy,
drama therapy, movement/dance therapy, and more, understands that people can heal trauma through creative expression. You can find different expressive arts therapists in your
area on Psychology Today.
- Eye Movement Desensitization and Reprocessing (EMDR)
is a detailed protocol that helps people activate their natural
ability to heal from trauma. Some studies show that 84%-
90% of single-trauma victims no longer have post-traumatic
stress disorder after only three 90-minute sessions. https://
www.emdr.com/
- Energy Healing is a catch all for a wide variety of modalities
including Reiki and acupuncture that seek to help people
heal by removing energetic blocks. Emotional Freedom
Technique (EFT), or tapping is a series of simple exercises
you can learn and do on your own to work with your body's
energy and healing capacity. https://www.thetappingsolution.
com You can also do Reiki on yourself but it takes more
training. https://www.reiki.org
- Tension, Stress, and Trauma Release (TRE) is "a series of
exercises that assist the body in releasing deep muscular
patterns of stress, tension and trauma. The exercises safely
activate a natural reflex mechanism of shaking or vibrating
that releases muscular tension, calming down the nervous
system. When this muscular shaking/vibrating mechanism is
activated in a safe and controlled environment, the body

is encouraged to return back to a state of balance." https://
traumaprevention.com/
- Shamanic Journeying involves entering a trance-like state and visiting other realms to get guidance and information that might inform your healing. Every culture has had shamans, so there are many culturally-specific practices and ways of journeying. There is also a kind of modern secular shamanism, sometimes called neoshamanism. My suggestion is to seek out the shamanism of your ancestors if you can. You might find practicing shamans in your area or online, and there are also online classes and training programs in shamanic healing and journeying.
- Plant-Spirit Medicine is the "shamans' way with plants. It recognizes that plants have spirit and that spirit is the strongest medicine. Spirit can heal the deepest reaches of the heart and soul." https://plantspiritmedicine.org

For additional trauma education: Folks who identify as women might appreciate Kimberly Ann Johnson's book, *Call of the Wild: How We Heal Trauma, Awaken Our Own Power, and Use It For Good.* Irene Lyon has some great online content and programs on trauma and healing the nervous system. Peter Levine, Gabor Maté, Staci Haines, and Nadine Burke have written great books about trauma but there are many others. I think everyone should read or listen to Resmaa Menakem's *My Grandmother's Hands: Racialized Trauma and the Pathway to Mending Our Hearts and Bodies* for education on intergenerational trauma and the tie between personal and collective racial healing.

Exercise & Reflection:

Choose one of the modalities mentioned in this section to try or research more.
- What appeals to you about it?
- How might you use it in your own healing journey?

Record this in your healing journal.

Build a Support Dream Team

Now that you have lots of healing tools to play with and you know what you're healing for (having written a vision in Section 1), we need to make sure you have some support to help you keep the dream alive and find success on the healing path. This section is both about supporting yourself and getting support from others—whether it's moral support or practical support, like asking someone to buy you groceries. If asking for help feels really hard for you right now, don't worry. We're going to talk about how to work with that.

As covered in the healing principles and throughout this book so far, healing happens in community. I can't stress enough how important it is to find your people and spend time with folks who get what you're going through. We're going to look at how you can cultivate community with folks you love, even if you can't get out of bed.

Modern American folklore would have us believe that there are a lot of things we "should" be able to do on our own, like start a business, or heal from a complex illness. But that's about as real as a jackalope riding a unicorn. In reality, no one, ever, in the history of the world, has achieved great things entirely on their own. Still, that reality hasn't stopped a lot of us from insisting that we can do things, or everything, on our own.

Some of it is about pride and wanting to be independent, sure, but also, asking for support can feel really scary. For some of us, it kicks up all kinds of worries and shame. I can't tell you how many people, when asked about calling in support say, "I could never…" But we lose a lot in resisting support. The resistance takes a lot of energy, no matter what form it takes. We expend a lot of energy—physical, emotional, and otherwise—trying to prove we don't need it. We might also experience a deep longing and sadness around not having support, wishing people would just know that we need it. We feel like we shouldn't have to ask. Or we feel like there is no one to ask.

There was a year in my mid-twenties when I regularly found myself sitting on my bed, essentially paralyzed, phone in hand, wanting to call a friend for support but sobbing uncontrollably, unable to press the dial button. I felt so ashamed and needy. I felt like I should be able to call my parents, that they ought to be able to take care of me in all aspects. They lived overseas at the time, and they also had no idea how bad things were because I didn't tell them. I worried that even if my friends were willing to listen to me or help me make dinner, which would have been a huge help, I wouldn't have been able to reciprocate, and that wouldn't be fair. I didn't want to be a burden and I worried that my friends would be scared of my truths, or think I was lying when I described my bizarre symptoms. Especially because my symptoms were largely invisible, I worried that folks wouldn't understand or would think I was nuts and write me off.

A few years later when I hired a life coach to help me figure out my next steps, the single best thing I got out of coaching was overcoming my fear of asking for support. It's been several years since then and, while I've made progress in asking for and receiving support, it is still sticky for me.

Like anything, it's a practice. I'm blessed to have a best friend who calls me out on the reciprocation worry and regularly reminds me that support in a friendship is neither transactional nor a quid-pro-quo affair. They remind me that they *want* to cook me dinner because it brings them joy, not because they think they'll get something out of it later. I'm still detoxing those American capitalist reciprocity and hyper-individualist narratives from my system.

However, I do want to acknowledge that some people won't understand why or how you need support. If someone has never had a severe or chronic health challenge, or a close friend or family member with one, they probably won't get it, at least at first. They may say things that are inadvertently hurtful and othering, and that can make it hard to ask them for support.

But, some people are trainable, and they don't necessarily need to understand to be helpful. You do need to be able to clearly communicate how you would like to be supported though, and that can be challenging if you don't feel good. I have recommended that my clients write a support manual for close friends and loved ones. Especially if you are someone who flares, it can be really nice for the folks close to you to know how to help when you can't talk or communicate clearly because of pain, brain fog, a panic attack, or something else. Your manual might address topics like preferred times to have space versus having company, favorite words of encouragement, or topics of conversation that they should bring up or avoid. You might also include very practical information like doctors' contact info or a list of foods you like if someone can cook or shop for you. Your people will be grateful to know how they can help.

In my quest to master the art of asking for support, I decided I wanted to build an official support team. First-time entrepreneurs or other high achievers will often build a personal board of directors to guide them in business and career choices. This is a similar idea but rather than helping me with business or career goals, I wanted a team to support me in my healing, namely in making the whole process of living and working with a chronic illness easier and more fun.

I convened my "Support Dream Team" at first to support me in transitioning back to working and living on my own after eight months of being unemployed and living with family in Virginia. After my parents moved back from overseas, we had a come-to-Jesus conversation that resulted in them hosting me. While a little challenging at first, living with my parents was overall a very nourishing and supportive experience.

My mom did all the cooking, which was an enormous blessing, so I was freed up to do a lot more resting. After living with my family, and feeling somewhat stronger and healthier, I planned to move back to Boston to live with my partner at the time. I worried about putting too much pressure on him, especially because I wasn't working very much, was still having debilitating daily headaches, taking lots of naps, going to many doctors appointments, and eating a pretty complicated anti-inflammatory diet—hence the desire for additional support.

I did not like the idea of asking people for help, particularly for basic needs like laundry, grocery shopping, and feeding myself, but, with the support of my coach at the time, I saw that I had a few people in my life who would probably be happy to help. I wrote an email to my five closest friends in Boston explaining that I was excited to be moving back, wanted to see them, and I was still feeling pretty sick and in need of support while I got back into the routine of city life and working. Would they be willing to help me in the following X, Y, and Z ways? It was really scary, until I got really sweet responses back.

One friend volunteered to cook me dinner at least once a month. Another friend took me out to dinner a whole bunch, at places with menus that worked for me, and always picked up the tab. For a long time that was the extent of my "going out," and it was a real gift to me. A couple other friends helped me move three different times in the eighteen months after my initial email. All these friends have told me that they're grateful that I asked them for support, because previously they'd wanted to help but didn't know how.

They were happy to have concrete ways to make things easier for me, and helping out gave them another way to spend time with me. Despite all my worries that I'd ask for too much, be rejected, and end up alone, I'm still friends with all the folks on my original Support Dream Team. And, now that I'm feeling better, I have more energy to support them, something I worried I wouldn't be able to do. I even helped several of my support team members move, which is about the most energy-intensive thing one can do for a friend!

If it's not yet clear, I am so enamored with the power of support that it's become a big part of my coaching work. I always seek to have clients finish their coaching contracts with rich and diverse networks of people who can support them in their healing, their careers, their hobbies, the change they want to make in the world, and more. Next, I've included steps and prompts here to help you create your own Support Dream Team and figure out what to ask of the members. You can center your team around your healing specifically, or things you want to change in your life as a whole.

1. **Get clear on your goals.** Revisiting your healing vision statement and writing out some goals would be a good first step here. Think of the goals as accomplishments that will both move your vision forward and bring you joy when you score them. If, for example, you want to start a meditation practice, a meditation-related goal might be to attend a day-long meditation retreat by a certain date. You'll probably want to establish a daily meditation practice before you go to the retreat. In this way the meditation goal will provide some motivation for you to live from your vision a little bit every day and keep up with your meditation practice.

2. **Identify the roles you want to fill.** Once you're clear on your goals and the support you'd love to be able to score them, you can ask yourself, "Who do I need on my team to help me make this vision real?" This will allow you to start building a roster for your dream team. List out all the tasks/projects you want support with. In the meditation example it might sound like, "accountability buddy to text me every day and make sure I meditated" or "someone to drive me to and from meditation group" or "a meditation teacher who

can teach me how to meditate comfortably given my body's needs."

You can also create general roles for day-to-day support, for example, someone to get you groceries, someone willing to do food prep for an hour with you once a week, a spoonie buddy with whom you can have weekly kvetching and emotional support calls.

3. **Begin filling in the team roster.** Once you have your list of roles, start by filling in any obvious ones, e.g. Chief Cheerleader: Zainab, Walking Buddy: Mitch, Recipe Recommender: Nando.

The people on your team can be professionals, friends, or volunteers. There are time banking and mutual aid groups on Facebook, and elsewhere online, where you can ask for support from the community, or offer it. NextDoor can also be a good resource for connecting with people in your neighborhood.

Don't worry about having specific people to fill every role right away. Taking your healing, or anything, to the next level of ease or awesomeness is going to require you to build some new relationships. If you could do everything you wanted without asking for support or cultivating new relationships, you probably would have done it already.

It may take time to fill some of the roles on your Dream Team and you may have to replace people over time as they move, have babies, get busy, get sick, travel, etc. As challenging as it may seem to make new relationships when you don't feel well, once you have them, you may find that some or all of them are super rewarding and mutually beneficial in ways you never imagined possible.

One of my Lyme buddies sought me out when she was looking for support via our local Lyme group. I think she mostly wanted to connect with another young person who understood what she was going through. She's turned out to be a super big support in *my* life, and I love her to death as a friend. Even though we don't see each other that often, when we do, it's always a breath of fresh air.

She's a little bit older than me, married, a homeowner in the Boston suburbs, now a mother, and someone with a beautiful eye for design. She called me every Monday when I moved in with my parents. Next to my partner, she was the person who supported me the most and really kept me going when I felt isolated and worried that I would never get better.

A couple years later, when I had to move unexpectedly because of a mold problem, she took me to Home Goods and bought me a bunch of new kitchen supplies like a magical fairy godmother. She's an amazing human and I'm not sure we ever would have connected if it wasn't for Lyme. We are still buds and have found many things to talk about outside of antibiotics and treatment protocols, though it's really nice to be able to talk shop about those things too.

4. **Note any holes in the roster and brainstorm how you might find and get support from those people.** If you don't already have a practitioner you need in your neighborhood,

who could you ask for recommendations? What support groups, spiritual communities, networking groups, listervs, or online communities could you consult for leads? Is there a resource center or clinic that services your health challenge(s) specifically? Are you willing to post on social media to solicit ideas from friends, colleagues, or fellow spoonies?

If you are looking to work with healers but unsure how to cover the cost, what could be accessible for you? Can you learn tips and practices on YouTube and free online resources? Can you find healers who are willing to do trades or work on a sliding scale? Are there community clinics in your area that offer free or low-cost care, such as community acupuncture?

Where I lived in Western Massachusetts there is both a community acupuncture clinic (sessions are $30) and a free clinic called the People's Medicine Project that offers acupuncture for early recovery from opioids, body work, herbal medicine, homeopathy, and art therapy. Learn more at https://www.peoplesmedicineproject.com/.

5. **Ask for support!** Start with easy asks and ask people who are likely to say "yes." This will help build your confidence and give you a chance to practice sharing your vision before you try to enroll the support of people you don't know, or people you know less well. If asking for help feels hard, get some support around that. Ask a friend who's good at lovingly kicking your butt. Consult an elder, mentor, or leader in your community, or hire a coach to help you overcome whatever is making it hard to ask for help.

Asking for help is a common challenge and other people have struggled with it too. (Many coaches have sliding scales, scholarships, and pro-bono offerings, so money need not be a barrier to getting support.)

If you're asking friends and/or family for support, sometimes it can feel nice to make the ask to a larger group, then follow up with people individually. This might look like an email or a WhatsApp group message titled, "Be on my Dream Team?" If there's anything you need to communicate to a wide audience like "I'm not going to be able to hang out as much while I'm focused on the next phase of my healing" or "I would love it if you asked me about X when we talk" then you can do that at the same time.

When one of my rockstar clients and now dear friend, Lindsay Wolff, was feeling particularly isolated at home, often too sick to go out, she wrote an email to all her best girlfriends asking them to come hang out with her. She provided a list of things she'd like to do, i.e. crafting, watching rom coms, just chatting and catching up, and she got a great response.

With her permission, I'm including her email here:

Hi Best Girls:

As part of my work as a coach and as a recipient of coaching, I'm doing a lot of work learning to ask for exactly what I'd love as I go through Lyme treatment. It's vulnerable and scary work, but I'm doing it because I'm ready to drop the I'm-fine-don't-wor ry-about-me-I-don't-need-anyone attitude. I totally need people! This is hard!

So, a simple step I'm taking to relieve myself of the pressure to be so poised and perfect while I heal is to make a simple ask of my dearest girlfriends: I need standby Hangout Buddies.

I really want Nate to be able to be his free-spirited rasta man self, and that means a lot of weekends I'm on the couch while he's out doing his thing - which I want! I need him to keep living life! But I'm not going to act like it's not sometimes lonely and sad.

So, I'm asking friends who are in the know about my health struggle to come over and expect nothing more than TV and hammock time and hot tea. Just presence.

I often resist asking because I don't want to explain how badly I feel and get into it, and writing this email relieves me of that conversation. I just want to be able to text people and say, I'm not doing well, can you come over and watch Bridget Jones Diary with me?

I know you're probably thinking, of course, Lindsay! But I realize I'm not taking enough people up on their willingness to be with me when I'm low and I want to crack open my life and struggle just a little bit more.

So, if you're interested in being a Hangout Buddy, just reply to me.

If your life is insane and you're moving and you work a million hours a week and your baby is teething, please decline. You're still my dear one, our friendship doesn't change at all. I just want to get a read on who is interested and available for this kind of activity.

On a happy note, I want to say that my treatment is going REALLY well all things considered. It's still wickedly uncomfortable, and I cry almost everyday, but I'm seeing signs of life that I haven't been able to experience in a long time. I am feeling confident I will make a full recovery - it's just going to take time. Thanks for your love and support.

Lifting my organic turmeric ginger tea in cheers,
Lindsay

How vulnerable and beautiful is that? You can see why her friends said "yes" to her ask!

Once you've filled in the more obvious slots on your support team roster, you can move on to filling the remaining open spots. Depending on what kind of people you're looking for, you might be able to find them through internet research or asking around. You might also need to do some networking to find the people you're seeking. Before you scream and go running for the hills at the mention of the word "networking," let me remind you that I'm also a career coach and I've got some tips for you.

When you're reaching out to people you don't know, or don't know well, try to be really clear with them about what you're asking for. First, get super clear about what you're asking for, whether it's a recommendation for a certain kind of professional or organization, articles, resources, or some other aspect of their expertise. Whenever possible, research the person before you reach out and demonstrate that you've done so, like saying, "I really appreciated your blog post on baby goat yoga."

This shows respect for their work and their time. Then follow that up with a specific question, "Do you know of any baby goat yoga classes in the Milwaukee area?" Assume that people want to support you and share their expertise with you. Wouldn't you? Some people won't want to help or won't have the spoons, and that's okay. When someone says they can't help, or they simply never get back to you, nine times out of ten, that has nothing to do with you or your ask. And make sure you follow up! At least once. Do you respond to every single email, voicemail, and message you get on all your social media platforms always, on the first message? If so, you get a trophy. A lot of us don't.

Remember that if someone doesn't respond, that doesn't mean they were offended by your message or don't like you. It could mean that, but more likely it means that your message is drowning in their crowded inbox, or they're on vacation, or they just had a baby, or have been living through a difficult health challenge of their own. Definitely follow up. Building a team takes time. Even if you needed support yesterday, be patient with yourself and others. Play the long game on this one.

6. **Practice asking your team for support regularly.** When you encounter challenges or see opportunities to do things with more ease, ask yourself, "Is there someone on my support team who might love to help me with this?" Should you have moments when asking for support feels hard (likely!), remember that people who kick a lot of ass in life are people who have mastered the art of giving and receiving support.

If you do not already have a spoonie hero that you look up to, I suggest looking out for one you admire—someone you can hold up as a reminder that healing happens with support. My spoonie hero is Missy Elliott, who hit a big road bump in her career after getting diagnosed with a thyroid condition.

She took her healing seriously, got a lot of support, and has continued to grace us with incredible music. And even if she wasn't a spoonie, there's no way she could have become the hip-hop legend she is, the original Queen Bee, without getting a few different kinds of support. It helps for example, that she's childhood friends and longtime collaborators with producer Timbaland.

It's also really important to have people in your life who really get it—folks you can kvetch with and who can laugh with you and make light of the absurd experience of living with a chronic condition inside a system that isn't built to accommodate it. Over the years I've made a lot of friends with Lyme, but there are five who I still talk to regularly. I'll contact different folks for different things like moral support, questions about treatment protocols, or accountability for sticking to self-care routines.

One of my Lyme buddies is also my book buddy, and she has been instrumental in getting this book out of my head and onto the page. These buddies bring immense joy to my life, and my friendships with them have become some of my most treasured relationships. I found one Lyme friend through a Boston Lyme support group, two through my coaching community, one through a friend of a friend, and I met another at a writing workshop for folks with chronic illness. If you don't yet have buddies who share your health challenge(s), I suggest you make it a priority to find some.

Look for local support groups, ask your practitioners if they know folks who might love to connect with you, or look in online support groups. Online relationships can even blossom into in-person relationships if you're in the same place and have the spoons to meet up. One of my most treasured Lyme buddies is someone I have never met in person. Yet I love her deeply and know I can call/text her anytime about pretty much anything. If you don't yet have buds like this in your life, or you want more, set an intention to make these connections and be open to them showing up in ways you don't expect!

Reflection Questions:
- How do you feel about the support you currently have in your healing?
- If you're interested in enrolling more support, what action(s) are you willing to take to bring more people in?
- Who might love to be on your team?
- If you currently don't have many close people in your life, how could you connect with some new folks?

Record your answers in your healing journal.

Cultivate Self-Love

"What's love but a secondhand emotion? What's love got to do, got to do with it? Who needs a heart when a heart can be broken?"

—Tina Turner

"Love is not something we give or get, it is something that we nurture and grow, a connection that can only be cultivated between two people when it exists within each of them—we can only love others as much as we love ourselves."

—Brené Brown

"Whatever arises, love that."

—Matt Kahn

This chapter looks at what it means to love yourself and how to practice doing it. Because we are all connected, loving yourself also means loving the collective. I suggest seven practices to support you in loving all of yourself, offer approaches to loving yourself by loving your community, and recommend resources that might support you in healing from a more loving place. I am sharing healing modalities and frameworks that have helped me love and respect myself more—but please remember that I am coming from a super privileged white girl perspective. If you got sick because of the stress of state-sponsored abuse on your body, like your community was poisoned or your family member was killed by a police officer, you might find your self-love practices to be different. Working with your community for justice can be a self-love practice. Organizing can be a self-love practice. Making dinner for loved ones or neighbors in need can be a self-love practice. Lobbying an elected leader can be a self-love practice. What I share in this chapter are just some suggestions. They won't be the right fit for everyone. You get to define what self-love means to you. Love comes in many forms, and I trust you to find and do what you need to earn your own love and respect, and support others around you to do the same. If it's ever not clear, your intuition, ancestors, and/or spirit can help you identify what will be the most loving choices for you.

It's part of the human condition to want to be loved. Part of what makes the experience of chronic illness so incredibly painful is how isolating it can be—how love, and being truly seen and heard, can feel out of reach. Even if you have loving relationships with people in your life, chances are most of them don't get how hard it is to live with health challenges and how challenging it can be to have your whole life revolve around meeting your body's special needs.

It's hard for anyone to understand unless they've experienced it themselves, and even if someone has had a similar experience, everyone's journey is different. You might be frustrated that people in your life don't know how to help. In the same way that people often expect their significant others to know what they need in a romantic partnership, it is common for us spoonies to expect family members and caregivers to know what we need in our healing. When we're already in pain or exhausted, it sucks to have to tell someone or teach them what to do and say, sometimes multiple times. We feel like we shouldn't have to do that.

There might also be people in your life who don't believe you. And/ or they might not be able to handle the discomfort, yours or their own, of never-ending pain, so they check out. I've seen more illness-related divorces than I can count, and I've seen parents in complete denial of their child's condition. Some spoonies lose everyone in the process of getting sick.

Unfortunately, our mainstream culture does not have good rituals or systems to care for folks with chronic illness, or to support their caregivers. As Johanna Hedva points out in her essay "Sick Woman Theory," our cultural expectation is that illness and injuries are temporary, and when they aren't, we don't know what to do, and neither do the folks around us. Some people get frustrated and bail. All of this compounds the already isolating experience of living with a health challenge.

For whatever reason, sometimes the love we want just isn't available, or it comes with fire and brimstone, and we can end up feeling like Tina Turner says—like love is too painful to even welcome in when our hearts can be broken. If you're already sick and in pain all the time, who wants a broken heart on top of that? So many of us long to be loved, look externally for something to fill our aching insides, and the longing adds a whole bunch of additional pain to the experience of having chronic health challenges.

Thankfully there are other options! We can ask others to love us the way we want to be loved, we can connect to divine love (see Disconnect and Reconnect chapter), and we can love the crap out of ourselves. In the best-case scenario, you're doing all three, but loving yourself is a prerequisite for the other two because you have to love yourself at least a little bit to feel worthy of receiving love.

And, at the end of the day, the person most qualified to love you is you. You can choose to be the one person who will never abandon you. It is something many of us have to grow into. Some of us get sick precisely because we abandon ourselves, and that too is something that can be healed and loved.

This section is one of the heftiest in the book because learning to love all of yourself fiercely is a really important aspect of healing yourself and being able to facilitate healing for those around you. It will make healing easier and more effective. Loving yourself is a crucial part of deprogramming oppression and healing the underlying trauma that causes disease.

This is because you need to be able to love yourself enough to go against the well-worn grain of your own patterning and societal norms. You need to be able to say, while many folks around me are doing this, I am going to do that, because that is what's most authentic to me and my healing. It requires a lot of courage and love to do that repeatedly.

Recognizing where and when you're not loving yourself can allow you to make tweaks and bring a whole lot more ease to your healing journey. Conversely, not loving yourself can manifest in ways that make you more susceptible to illness. Acting without self-love can look like not taking care of your physical or mental health, staying in abusive relationships, staying in toxic work environments, chronically putting others' needs before your own, chronic worrying, self-doubt, overworking, substance abuse, denying yourself pleasure, and on and on. It can also manifest as hyper independence.

When some part of us feels uncomfortable with being loved, we don't let it in and we push it away. We insist on doing everything on our own and any kind of praise or love makes us deeply uncomfortable. It's kind of like putting up an anti-love forcefield. It creates this reinforcing painful cycle of desperately wanting love but not allowing it in.

I am a hyper-independent, overachieving workaholic in recovery. More than twenty years into my healing journey I'm still waking up to how much I've abused myself because I wasn't loving myself or letting others love me. At some point my unconscious mind, and/or my nervous system, decided that love wasn't safe and that I didn't deserve it, so I repeatedly denied myself love and joy, and put myself in situations that maintained a comfortable but, in hindsight, harmful status quo.

In addition to working way too much, I dated people who, for one reason or another, couldn't love me the way I wanted to be loved or were easy to keep at a distance. I blocked love from family and friends because I was ashamed, feeling like love and support weren't something I should need or ask for. This rejection of love and care was compounded by a sense of guilt about my privilege and feeling as if I had a mandate to put myself aside and devote my life to uplifting others. As you can imagine, that didn't work for me and it's a huge part of why I burned out four times.

Organizing and changemaking work can be healing and empowering, but not if we're acting in a misaligned way, purely out of a sense of obligation and/or at the expense of our own joy. After my fourth burnout, I finally asked for help, let my family take care of me for a little while, and used what savings I had to hire a coach because I knew I needed help to break the cycle I was in. After I finally slowed down, I started to realize that on an unconscious level, my illness was a vehicle for me to heal this pattern.

I needed to give myself permission to rest and get some of the love I longed for and didn't know how to get any other way. I didn't love seeing that, but humans adapt to their environment in all kinds of ways to get what they need. It's in our biology. I recognize now that my body and soul were trying to take care of me the best way they saw fit at the time, given my own resistance. I am getting better at resting, asking for what I need, and having my own back. I also still mess up, and then I try to practice loving the mess-ups and the lessons I learn from them.

I certainly don't believe that all sick people are unconsciously making themselves sick to get love (many people are sick because our systems are violent and oppressive) but I have connected with other spoonies or former spoonies who think their illness was in part a way for them to get the love they weren't giving themselves. Once they accepted that their illness was a conduit for getting the love they wanted, and they saw that they were in fact the only ones who could give themselves the love they needed, everything changed for them, and they were able to make great progress in their healing.

That's been my experience too. The process of taking ownership for loving myself and caring for myself has been a bumpy ride. It felt easier, and certainly more socially acceptable, to blame the bacteria, the concussion, and to be angry at all the doctors who misdiagnosed me when they were supposed to help me. Expressing that anger has been really important, in tandem with learning to love all of myself—the parts that wanted to be loved, the parts that were angry, and the parts that were upset that I didn't figure all this out sooner. Recognizing this helped me move forward.

It's not necessarily intuitive that if something feels bad or isn't working, you should practice loving it more. But that's exactly how it works. Love is the medicine for every struggle, pain, and fuck up. Practicing with this medicine might look like caring for yourself, being gentle with yourself, practicing self-compassion when you make a mistake, or choosing (if you can) to remove yourself from situations that aren't serving you. For more on this, I highly recommend Matt Kahn's book, *Whatever Arises, Love That.* In addition to outlining how to love all parts of yourself, he specifically speaks to how loving yourself can help heal an overstimulated nervous system, which, let's be honest, is probably part of the picture for all of us on some level.

Part of what's inspired me to work on loving myself is knowing many people have struggled with it, committed to it, and become beautiful beings with so much to share on the other side. I have never met someone with a significant health challenge who didn't also at some point struggle with loving themselves. I mean, in our society, who doesn't? But some folks, because of trauma in this lifetime, a past one, or in the genes we've been passed from our ancestors, experience a lower sense of self-worth, and find it harder to love themselves. It's no coincidence that the folks who are the sickest for the longest are often survivors of abuse, assault, state violence, ongoing oppression, or sexual violence that they have not had the opportunity to metabolize.

When left unhealed, that kind of trauma does a number on your self-worth. And it's harder to love yourself if you don't feel worthy of love, or if someone totally f-ed up your understanding of what love is. There are so many reasons why people can get sick, stay sick, and struggle to act in their own self-interest. This is why both illness and self-love deficits will show up differently in different people. It is also why different bodies need different paths to healing.

Some folks also have more difficulty healing because they have been conditioned by society and/or their families to see themselves as less than. It's hard to love yourself when everyone has given you the message that you're not worth loving. Personally, I experienced some harmful programming around what a woman should be to be loved. There is a lot of anti-self-love messaging specific to folks with marginalized identities, and for Black, Indigenous, queer, trans, and disabled people in particular.

As I've mentioned elsewhere in the book, it can be especially sweet to heal in community with folks who share your identities, and cultivating love is no exception. Sometimes self-love is achieved by coming together and practicing community love and collective care.

In a February 2021 public Zoom conversation between Harvard Kennedy School Professor Khalil Gibran Muhammad and long-time community organizer and voting rights activist LaTosha Brown, Professor Muhammad asked Ms. Brown how her organization Black Voters Matter helped win multiple democratic victories in Georgia in the 2020 election. She said, "We created a campaign around Black voters and our candidate was Black power."[89] The strategy was built on helping Black folks see that they had agency, that they were already powerful, and that they could change the narrative that Black votes are transactional. Ms. Brown underscored that these campaigns were a significant healing experience for Black folks in the South in particular,

89 Susan A. Hughes, "History, Activism, and the Power of Black Voters," Harvard Kennedy School, February 16, 2021, https://www.hks.harvard.edu/faculty-research/policy-topics/gender-race-identity/history-activism-and-power-black-voters.

who have experienced generations of programming around being invisible—and were raised with an understanding that visibility and gains in Black power *always* come with violent or deadly white backlash.

I include this anecdote because I think it's a beautiful example of how organizing can be healing and how impactful it can be for individuals and communities to see how incredible and worthy they are. While the goal of the campaign was to elevate Black voices and votes, the tactic was cultivating self and community love and connection. Ms. Brown's organizing work lifts up individual voices by centering collective love.

Sometimes it is more accessible to love your community first, and through your community's love, see just how lovable you are. Some ways to access community love include activism, volunteering, civic engagement, ceremony/ritual/memorial services, cultural events, support groups, social events for a specific neighborhood or identity (e.g. a locally organized queer picnic), mutual aid groups, community free stores, fundraisers, open mic nights, community health clinics, senior centers, healing justice collectives, disability justice groups, and resource centers for people who hold certain identities.

In Northampton, Massachusetts, the Lyme Disease Resource Center organizes support groups, workshops, movie screenings, and other events. Especially since the COVID-19 pandemic started, more and more community events are available online, making it easier to participate in community happenings even with low spoons.

We are fortunate to live in a time when more people are preaching the gospel of collective care and intentionally building communities of care. The tips I share are individual practices, but they can absolutely be done in community with the support of loved ones, in spiritual communities, in movement spaces, in the workplace, and otherwise. Since the COVID-19 pandemic brought most of our society to its knees, many people in this country are more open to the mutual giving and receiving of care outside the nuclear family.

I encourage you to look for opportunities to share the journey of healing and cultivating self-love with others and see if there are ways to bring a healing, love-centered focus to other parts of your life, whether it's at your job, in organizing, or care work. There are many paths to loving yourself more deeply. Doing it in community, particularly a community that shares your identity or experience, can be in itself a beautiful act of self-love.

Depending on your experiences, and what you feel has contributed to your illness, this could look like gathering a group of spoonies to support each other with the healing journey, or something more specific like starting or joining a support group for individuals with incarcerated family members, or individuals impacted by the opioid epidemic.

Until recently, I have done most of my self-love work in partnership with spoonie friends, or with healing practitioners. I understand that it has been an incredible privilege to have the resources to hire support. It is certainly not the only way to have self-love breakthroughs. Hiring help is a very white, professional class approach to solving problems, and in hindsight, I think I would have benefited from more community support earlier on.

Today, I greatly appreciate being part of a peer-counseling community focused on healing early wounds, detoxing societal programming, cultivating self-love, and reclaiming our innate healing intelligence. Next, I'll share more about what has helped me love myself more. If at any point you're not feeling it, or you feel triggered, feel free to skip down to the Practices for Boosting Self-Love.

My journey started with waking up each morning and taking a minute to hug myself and say, "I love you Noëlle." One of my favorite guiding questions even today is, "What would it look like to meet this situation from a place of loving myself?" I've also found it helpful to look for the parts of me that are the most resistant to love as a first step. You can think of it as a practice of making the unconscious conscious.

The aforementioned brain training and interrogating mental models can be part of this process, and it's awesome if you can find support in identifying and working with patterns that you might not even know are there.

After years of coaching and getting coached on how to observe and shift my attention, I made a lot of progress on getting out of my own way, but I felt like I had reached a plateau in my healing. I felt like there were some blocks to address that were beyond the reach of coaching. I went looking for more support.

What I found next was a practice called muscle testing, which ended up being one of the most helpful things I did to identify these unconscious blocks. Muscle testing, also known as Applied Kinesiology, is a way of testing the body's response to given stimuli. It is typically used by alternative health practitioners to identify how different substances might help or hurt a particular body. It's often used to identify allergies or to see if certain herbs or supplements are going to be helpful.

The process can look like holding a vial of pollen in your hand and holding your arm up to resist the practitioner as they try to push your arm down. If you can't resist the pressure, and they can push your arm, it means that substance isn't a good fit for you. In my work with this practitioner, we did the same thing but with words, to test my body's emotional response. I would hold my arm out and he'd say something like, "I believe my family wants me to heal," then push on my arm.

If I easily resisted his pressure, we could assume that all parts of me did in fact believe that my family wants me to heal. If he was easily able to push my arm down, we could assume that some part of my psyche did not believe that. Through this process, in just a couple sessions, we were able to identify, with eerie precision, the parts of my emotional being that were scared to be well and scared to be seen.

Once I saw these beliefs, I was able to process and work with them in different ways. I wrote poetry about what came up, I cried a lot, and I took some of what came up to a friend to talk through it. All these actions were immensely helpful in moving old energetic patterns that were keeping me sick. I think we only did four sessions together, but they were a massive game changer in my healing. Therapy, somatic coaching, and core energetics[90] have also helped me immensely with bringing consciousness to unconscious self-denigrating beliefs and supported me in my journey to love all parts of myself.

I love myself a whole lot more than I used to, but my body continues to push me to love more deeply and fully. Every time I reach a milestone in my healing and think, "I must be nearly there," I see that there's another horizon to reach, one that requires more love, more attention, more patience, and more acceptance. I don't think there's a finish line when it comes to loving ourselves. My friend Jack once told me that for him, self-love is like sailing. There are just things you need to do to keep the boat upright given the waves and changes in the weather.

I think it's safe to say self-love is a life-long practice and one that will change and grow with the curveballs life throws your way. Even though I know that in my bones, sometimes my reaction to being asked to love myself more is pretty whiny:

"Really, Body? But I already love you so much!"

Believe me, the whining doesn't help. I suspect my body will continue to ask for more love until there are no unloved shadows or hurt parts left. Or until new ones emerge at least. And that makes sense. When we're feeling guilt, shame, or beating ourselves up in any way, we deny ourselves what we need—either on purpose because we think we don't deserve it, or because we're too distracted by our own drama. Conversely, when we love ourselves fully and treat ourselves as we would our most favorite person in the world, it's a lot easier for healing to happen, because we give ourselves what we need. Giving

---

90 Core Energetics is a synthesis of body-oriented psychotherapy and spiritual development. It brings consciousness to how we block our life energy by perpetuating defensive patterns adapted in childhood which keep us limited and disempowered. https://www.coreenergetics.org/

ourselves what we need, consistently, with ease and grace, requires us to be our own beloved.

Easier said than done, obvi. We all come out of the womb pure, but as soon as we start experiencing a sense of self, systems of oppression teach us that we're less than others. We start building a list of things we don't get to have, and another list of things we don't like about ourselves. I wish we could all wake up one morning and say, "Okay, Self. I love you. Let's do this life thing!! I'm going to support you 100%." I imagine that works for some folks, but for most of us, cultivating self-love is more of a heroine's journey, especially because really loving yourself is still radical in our culture. I love that the self-love imperative is becoming more mainstream (thank you Lizzo, Queer Eye, and others!) but there is a lot of room for the trend to grow.

Historically, it has been cool in our society to beat yourself up in all manner of ways: doing extreme sports; drinking, which is basically a big F-you to your most important organ, the liver; being super busy; being self-deprecating. We don't see anyone getting props for hydrating well and going to bed on time, though that is my personal fantasy. Can you imagine going to a meeting on Monday morning at a startup and celebrating that everyone got a lot of sleep over the weekend?

High fives all around! So, given that it's not yet a widely accepted cultural norm, practicing self-love may require you to practice the art of not giving a fuck about what other people think. If you've already been sick or in pain or both for a while, you're probably getting good at this. Chronic discomfort helps us get really clear on what's important and what is not. I'll share more about that in the coming pages, but if you're still new to this journey, I invite you to notice what matters more to you: Is it more important to do what you need to take care of yourself or is it more important to manage others' discomfort? We can spend a lot of energy trying to keep others comfortable and it limits us from speaking our truths and doing what we truly need to do to heal. Being on the healing path means looking out for number one, Baby.

Other people and their expectations aside, learning to love the crap out of yourself may be one of the hardest journeys you'll face as a human being because of the internal work it requires. At times it will feel very uncomfortable, and you might feel like you can't handle it, but you can. You are so much stronger than you think you are. You will also have more support than you think you do.

You'll have many teachers—literal teachers but also, if you're willing to see everything as a healing and growing opportunity, teachers will come in the form of people you don't get along with, unexpected life changes, messages from your ancestors, and your body's reactions, among other things. It is important to be willing to come back to self-love when you fall off the wagon, because you will. You might be thinking, "I love myself. I'm good."

But no matter where you are in your healing journey, chances are you can probably love yourself a little more. Most of us receive A LOT of programming from culture and society that there is something wrong with us and we are not worthy of love—so unless we live very remotely, we're constantly swimming in anti-self-love waters. This is part of why self-love is a lifelong commitment. The negative reinforcement never ceases. We just get better at not taking it on.

Since it's been so helpful for me, it's my wish for everyone to have a mentor or buddy, or several, on their journey with self-love. It could be a friend, sibling, therapist, coach, community healer, spiritual advisor, mentor, or family/community member. If you don't already have someone in your life who could support you, I want to invite you to put the word out that you're looking for someone. Write down what you're looking for, tell some people about it, ask who they know, pray on it, and trust that the right person will come into your life. For something as big and unwieldy as learning to love yourself fully, it's so good to have support, and simply choosing not to do it alone could be your first self-love breakthrough.

For us spoonies in particular, practicing self-love is a tremendous contribution to those around you. As a result of loving yourself more, you might come to be more accepting of yourself and your situation. You might also become more courageous about standing up for yourself and/or your community as you see how worthy and deserving you are.

The more you love yourself, the more you might find you have more energy (since you're not spending it beating yourself up), so you can share more with the world and have more space for other people. As Brené Brown states in the quote at the start of this chapter, self-love is a crucial prerequisite to loving others with a full heart. Loving yourself can help you be a more loving parent, child, sibling, partner, friend, family member, neighbor, and coworker. When you love yourself, you're able to show up for others without getting as entangled in their suffering.

Practices for Boosting Self-Love
1. Mirror work and affirmations
2. Loving-kindness meditation
3. Write a love letter to your self
4. Get real with your inner critic
5. Create a loving partnership with your body
6. Practice pleasure
7. Say "no" to others and "yes" to yourself

I want to invite you to try out these practices, do what resonates and feel free to skip what doesn't.

Mirror Work and Affirmations

It has helped me so much to practice looking in the mirror every day and saying "I love myself." That is just one affirmation that you can play with. I suggested others in the Train Your Brain section. What

I'm sharing here are self-love affirmations—a statement that you say to affirm a truth about yourself in a supportive and encouraging way. You can say affirmations about whatever you really need to hear.

Here is a practice you can play with to come up with a personalized affirmation just for you: When you are relaxed and feeling relatively grounded, perhaps after meditating or before going to sleep at night, or first thing in the morning, take a moment to ask your body, "What do you need to hear from me right now?" Take some deep breaths and notice what comes up.

If you hear, "I need to know I'm sexy," for example, you can turn that into an affirmation like "I am a sexy motherfucker," and repeat it to yourself while looking in the mirror for a few days. Then notice what it feels like in your body when you're saying it to yourself. It might feel awkward at first, or uncomfortable, or awesome. Resist the urge to control the feeling and see if you can be open and curious about it.

The mirror can be a powerful tool in any number of ways. I have enjoyed at different times dancing naked in front of a full-length mirror, or standing in front of it and simply taking myself in. I also like to look at some part of my body that feels "off" in some way, or outside conventional beauty standards, and send love directly to that body part. Since I still have some lingering gut issues, I'll often stand in front of the mirror naked and rub my super bloated belly with a smile on my face and hold it lovingly as if I was a proud pregnant momma, channeling Demi Moore on the cover of *Vanity Fair* in 1991.

I still don't love my belly *all* the time, but I feel like I'm moving in that direction. It can also be nice to just move in front of the mirror. If it's accessible to you to do some movement seated or standing, take a few minutes to move in whatever way your body wants to and simply observe yourself. Try looking yourself in the eyes for some of it. This can be a very powerful way to reconnect with yourself if something or someone has thrown you off, or you feel like you've been sucked into another person's energy storm.

Loving-Kindness Meditation

Metta, or loving-kindness meditation, is a Buddhist practice for cultivating love and compassion for yourself and others. It's something you can do every day, even a couple times a day. It is essentially the practice of directing warm, loving feelings at yourself and others.

Sharon Salzberg, one of the modern fairy godparents of this practice, says the following about metta and its benefits in in *Loving-kindness: The Revolutionary Art of Happiness:*[91]

> We form the intention in our mind for our happiness and the happiness of all. This is different from struggling to fabricate a certain feeling, to create it out of our will, to make it happen. We just settle back and plant the seeds without worrying about the immediate result. That is our work. If we do our work, then manifold benefits will surely come.

> Fortunately, the Buddha was characteristically precise about what those benefits include. He said that the intimacy and caring that fill our hearts as the force of lovingkindness develops will bring eleven particular advantages:

> 1) You will sleep easily. 2) You will wake easily. 3) You will have pleasant dreams. 4) People will love you. 5) Devas [celestial beings] and animals will love you. 6) Devas will protect you. 7) External dangers [poisons, weapons, and fire] will not harm you. 8) Your face will be radiant. 9) Your mind will be serene. 10) You will die unconfused. 11) You will be reborn in happy realms.

Not too shabby for a list of possible side effects, am I right?

---

91 Sharon Salzberg, Loving Kindness: The Revolutionary Art of Happiness (London: Shambhala, 1995).

I am not a meditation teacher or devout Buddhist by any means, but I'll do my best to describe the practice as I learned it. A basic set of instructions from the book *The Issue at Hand* by Gil Fronsdal, can be found online via the Metta Institute.[92] Metta meditations are also available on Insight Timer, YouTube, and elsewhere online if you want to listen to something you can follow along with. If you have the spoons, you might also enjoy connecting with a meditation center to learn formal practice.

After reading the description that follows, I recommend putting the book down for a moment and giving this a try right away.

If you're able, sit in a comfortable position (I've also practiced lying down) and start by taking a few big breaths with long, slow, and complete exhalations. As you do so, imagine the energy of the breath moving into your chest and the space around your heart.

Metta is first practiced towards the self since it can be challenging to love yourself. Sitting quietly you can repeat, out loud or in your mind, the following phrases:

"May I be happy. May I be well. May I be free from suffering."

You might say it a couple times as you direct loving feelings toward yourself, continuing to breathe deeply.

After doing that for a bit, bring to mind someone you love a whole lot, perhaps a friend of family member, and direct loving-kindness toward them:

"May you be happy. May you be well. May you be free from suffering."

Then bring to mind someone you've encountered but don't know as well, like a bus driver or checkout clerk at a local store, and direct loving-kindness towards them. Then do the same for someone you don't like or are having a hard time with.

To cap the whole thing off, you may direct loving-kindness to all beings.

---

92 "Metta Institute," accessed February 2, 2023, https://www.mettainstitute.org/.

"May all beings be happy. May all beings be well. May all beings be free from suffering."

What do you feel in your body after doing the practice? I find it to be very effective in bringing out all the warm fuzzies.

Once you've practiced metta some, if you're feeling saucy and have the spoons for sexy time with yourself, you can experiment with the practice of erotic metta, which involves doing the same practice described above while pleasuring yourself. It involves breathing erotic energy from your genitals up into your heart space. I personally found the practice very uplifting, expansive, and pleasurable. A full description of the practice can be found in a publication called "Orgasmic Yoga Meditations."[93]

Write a Love Letter to Yourself

Unfortunately, in the digital age, love letters have fallen out of fashion. The new love letter is a text, a voice memo, perhaps a video if we're lucky, or an email if the sender is feeling old school. Back in the day, especially when lovers were not in the same place, they would write letters to each other to share their feelings and longings. Wikipedia defines the love letter as follows:

"A love letter is a way to express feelings of love in written form. Whether delivered by hand, mail, carrier pigeon, or left in a secret location, the letter may be anything from a short and simple message of love to a lengthy explanation of feelings."[94]

93 Joseph Kramer, "Orgasmic Yoga Meditations 2015," Erotic Massage, accessed February 23, 2023, https://www.eroticmassage.com/files/readings/OYMEDS2015.pdf.

94 "Love Letter," Wikipedia (Wikimedia Foundation, December 23, 2022), https://en.wikipedia.org/wiki/Love_letter.

A sweet self-love exercise is to write yourself a letter including all the things you appreciate, and maybe even love about yourself. Here are some prompts to get you started:

- If you were someone who loved the crap out of you, like a grandparent, sibling, or best friend, what might you say about yourself?
- What aspects of yourself are you proud of?
- What do you want to be acknowledged for?
- What makes you a badass?

Here is a love letter that I wrote to myself in a Gateless Writing retreat in May 2019:

Dear Noëlle,

You're awesome. I know you hear this from other people but I want you to hear it from these lips. You're such a freaking weirdo and you're perfect. I know it's been hard to feel like you never fit in and like the animals were the only ones who understood you. People are stupid sometimes and it's great that you're great with animals. There's a reason everyone wants you to dog sit.

One of the things I love about you is your ability to communicate, not just with animals, but also with folks who barely speak English, and with folks like B from Haiti who despite being in the U.S. for decades has an accent that too many Americans write off as too hard to handle.

Your patience is a true gift.

Sometimes I am surprised by just how patient you can be, and compassionate. I appreciate that you go out of your way to treat humans as humans and you usually catch yourself when you're not doing it. This is why random people come and talk to you, and why you mostly don't get fucked with. People can see that you're needed here, that your kind are good to keep around. And, as much as you might argue otherwise, I want to remind you just how freaking fearless you are and always have been, in so many ways. Remember how at age six you went to sleep away camp for two weeks and when your parents came to visit halfway through, you barely paid attention to them, more interested in your new friends and everything that was the freedom of having your own life? I know it didn't feel like a big deal to you but it's pretty big that you worked in the West Bank and Gaza as a 20 year old. And then you started your own business, as a sick person. I still can't believe you pulled that off, and also I can. Even though it doesn't make sense to you yet, there's a reason people gravitate to you. There are reasons why you were identified early as having leadership potential, and reasons why you were prom queen twice, despite not being friends with any of the so-called popular kids. There's a reason your 35-person sales team loved you. It's that you see the humanity in the bully as well as the nerd, and you're willing to love them all. And you wouldn't be able to love them if you didn't possess that love for yourself so remember that when the "I'm bad at self-love" monkey mind story creeps in.

Noëlle, Beth Ann Suggs,[95] one of the holiest of all living fairy godmothers told you on Tuesday that you are becoming her mini me. Do you know how freaking amazing that is?! Not that you need that affirmation to be perfect but what all these people are doing is just mirroring back your light. It's not about what you've done really, it's about how you be. I love how you be. I love the way you stare at the wall, the way you plant seeds wherever you go, the way you walk through the world.

Keep crushing it. I love your guts.

Love,

Me

It feels pretty frickin' vulnerable to include this in the book, so I hope it's helpful! I want to encourage you to write your own letter to yourself. Give it a try and notice what you feel when you read it.

---

95 Beth Ann Suggs is Dean of Students at the Academy of Coaching Excellence, a former Unity minister, and one of my coaching mentors.

Get Real With Your Inner Critic

A critical component of self-love practice is first noticing when you're beating up on yourself. Self-criticism is one of the biggest hindrances to human development and healing. If our inner dialogue is always something like, "You suck and can't do anything," it's going to be hard to do what you need to do to heal. Healing requires you to be an unapologetically outspoken advocate for yourself, and it's hard to do that if you don't believe you're worth it. But, before you beat yourself up for beating yourself up, let me assure you that it's normal. Everyone is mean to themselves.

The late metaphysical healer and author Louise Hay went so far as to say that we all hate ourselves on some level. I don't agree with everything she preached, but I do think she was on to something with the self-hatred thing. Our society makes it cool to beat yourself up,[96] but even if that wasn't true, our brains are literally wired to see the glass half empty. This phenomenon, known as the negativity bias, causes us to perceive negative information as more memorable than positive information. Rick Hanson, author of *Hardwiring Happiness: The New Brain Science of Contentment, Calm, and Confidence,* describes the negativity bias as "velcro for the bad, Teflon for the good."[97]

As I've discussed already, we can train our brains to notice and place more value on the good things in our lives, what we have, and what we're doing well. We can do that by continuously collecting evidence to support conclusions that are both true and supportive for us. This might look like cultivating gratitude, celebrating your successes, and learning to shift your attention from negative conclusions to more empowering ones. Mental models, which I talk about in Interrogate

---

96 I want to acknowledge here that society doesn't set everyone up to hate on themselves in the same way. People of color, people socialized as women, queer folks, trans folks, disabled folks, and other people with marginalized identities get a lot more self-critical programming than cis-hetero white men, for example. That said, cis-hetero white men are affected by toxic masculinity and social pressures to be tougher, better, faster, stronger, in charge always, able to drink more, etc. which certainly foster feelings of inadequacy as well.

97 Rick Hanson, Hardwiring Happiness: The New Brain Science of Contentment, Calm, and Confidence (New York: Harmony Books, 2016).

Your Mental Models, are an example of a conclusion, specifically a deeply held conclusion about how the world works. We have a lot of conclusions about ourselves, what we're good and bad at, what we're capable of, etc. Without even knowing it, we might be collecting evidence to support a conclusion that we are inept, a failure, or something similarly disempowering. A lot of us have a big old sack of evidence that we're not smart enough, not good enough, not strong enough, not pretty enough, or something like that, and we've been carrying that sack of evidence around and adding to it our whole lives.

When you're consistently adding evidence to the sack of things that are wrong with you, it's hard to believe anything on the contrary, like the possibility that you're a badass and can heal yourself. So even if you're not sure what it looks like, you're going to want to start collecting evidence for how awesome and capable you are, evidence that you can be your own healing hero. Adding evidence to *that* sack will create an inner landscape that is actually conducive to healing.

The first step in mastering this mindset shift is noticing who's doing the talking inside your head. We are complex creatures with lots of voices of inner dialogue. For the sake of learning this exercise let's say that at any given time you could be hearing and listening to one of two voices: your monkey mind or your voice of wisdom.[98]

"Monkey mind" is a Buddhist term for that inner dialogue we all experience that endlessly bounces between doubt and worry and shares its unsolicited critical opinion of everything. It's the negativity bias in action. Sometimes it's called the "inner critic," or gremlins, and yogis refer to it by its sanskrit name, chitta vritti. I heard another coach call it "your inner evil meanie."

Whatever you call it, it's probably located in the amygdala, the part of the brain that governs our fight, flight, or freeze response. When you're walking in the street and a car comes, your amygdala will help

---

98 This framework comes from the Academy for Coaching Excellence's coaching model created by Dr. Maria Nemeth. Learn more at https://acecoachtraining.com/ and in Dr. Nemeth's book, Mastering Life's Energies: Simple Steps to a Luminous Life at Work and Play.

you get out of the way. It may feel less useful when you're trying to decide what path to take next for medical treatment and you find yourself second-guessing every single option.

Dr. Maria Nemeth, founder of the Academy for Coaching Excellence, says monkey mind has the emotional maturity of a 9–11-year-old. It's always trying to make itself right and make everyone else wrong. As you start to pay more attention to your monkey mind, you may notice how immature it sounds, e.g. "That's hard." "He's prettier." "No one is going to want to be your friend."

The great thing about monkey mind though, is that it's not the whole truth. It can and often does contain grains of truth, but it's not the whole truth, though it would like you to believe otherwise. Monkey mind puts its own spin on the truth and presents the whole package as the truth. It isn't something that you can turn off or get rid of, but you can build the skill of observing it and shifting your attention so that it doesn't rule your life.

When you can see that you're passing judgment on yourself, and see that it is just monkey mind, it frees you up to see what's true. It cuts through the fog and the noise and allows you to hear your voice of wisdom, which comes from your intuition and your most deeply held values. Shifting your attention away from the monkey mind and toward your voice of wisdom can feel like taking blinders off and getting a whole new perspective.

It feels spacious and full of possibility. Let's say for example that you went to work sick with the flu. It might have been advisable to stay home, but you felt like you needed to be there to run a meeting. Maybe the meeting didn't turn out so great, and your monkey mind has a lot to say about how you could have been more prepared, how you suck at running meetings, and how you probably shouldn't be working in this industry at all.

But when you really look at the facts you might see that the truth is that yes, you *could* have handled that meeting better, but also you had the flu, and even Justin Timberlake's charming self would have struggled to win over those difficult clients with a foggy sick brain.

When you can see monkey mind for what it is in the moment, your amygdala trying to protect you from anything it perceives as unsafe or outside the status quo, then you can choose to gently shift your attention to observing what's actually true. It's a practice and something you'll need to choose again and again, kind of like meditation. In some styles of meditation you focus on the breath.

Your mind wanders. You notice your mind is wandering and you come back to the breath. We don't get better at meditating; we get better at noticing when we're not meditating. Same thing with monkey mind. We don't get better at making monkey mind go away (which would be useless because it never does go away). We get better at observing it and shifting our attention back to our voice of wisdom, what is true for us.

People who do big things in the world and appear to be free of worries and inhibitions have simply achieved a higher level of mastery when it comes to this observe-and-shift practice. I think it's also worth pointing out that some people, because of their life experience, may have had less monkey mind to begin with, and others, like trauma survivors, may hear their monkey mind much more often. But, everyone has it and everyone can change their relationship with it.

So how can you distinguish between monkey mind and your voice of wisdom? They feel really different. Like I said above, monkey mind sounds like a 9–11-year-old. It's fearful of change and always trying to maintain the status quo. It wants to keep you in your comfort zone and anything that threatens that will be presented as terrifying, or at least a bad idea. Monkey mind is limiting, and insistent that it's correct. Overthinking, second-guessing, scarcity, comparison, resignation, and justification are all symptoms of monkey mind.

Your voice of wisdom is more relaxed. It doesn't need to prove it's right because it just is. It feels spacious and full of possibility. The quality of it is abundant and generous. It may make you feel like you want to share things with other people. Your voice of wisdom is another name for your intuition.

Here is a handy chart my friend and mentor Zohar Tobi made, based on Dr. Maria Nemeth's teachings, to help you discern between monkey mind and voice of wisdom:

	Monkey Mind	Voice of Wisdom
Quality	Fearful, insistent, full of limitation	Creative, curious, full of possibility
Feeling	Contracted, tight, unsteady	Expansive, relaxed, engaged
Focus	Comfort, status-quo, self preservation	Growth, transformation, contributing to others
Effect	Closes your space	Opens your space

When you're feeling unsure about something, start by observing your own energy. Do you feel tight, contracted, or unsteady? That's a good indication that you're listening to a monkey mind conversation. It will leave you feeling drained and exhausted. Conversely, each time you shift your attention back to what is true for you and choose to consult and listen to your voice of wisdom, you will feel energized. Over time, as you master the art of seeing monkey mind and shifting your attention to your voice of wisdom, you will free up so much energy for healing!

Living your best life has become a popular meme in our time. You live your best life by listening to your voice of wisdom and consistently acting in ways that reflect your most important goals and values. This is also referred to as coherence or alignment. When you move through the world and take actions that are informed by your voice of wisdom, rather than your monkey mind, you are naturally acting in alignment, and alignment is love. Every action that you take that is informed by your voice of wisdom is an act of self-love. Taking action that is aligned with your voice of wisdom will create a really juicy sense of satisfaction because you're actually doing what you want, and showing up to it the way you want to, e.g., as a more centered, joyous human rather than a flailing, frustrated one.

This is a simple practice, but it will not feel easy, especially at first. Your monkey mind, wanting to maintain the status quo, will not give up easily. In fact, starting to do this work may cause a flurry of extra monkey mind at first. This is why it can be especially nice to get support from an ontological coach or Buddhist teacher. You might experience a lot of resistance to bringing on that kind of support, and that will just be the monkey mind trying to protect you from change, from the unknown. See if you can love it for trying to do its job. A way to get through the resistance is to ask a friend or loved one to hold you accountable for getting the support you want.

Supporting people with this practice of observing monkey mind and shifting their attention is a big part of my coaching work. In the beginning I do a lot of reflecting the monkey mind back to the client so they can see it. Then I guide them through ways of shifting their attention and seeing what is true. Throughout our time working together, a client will get better and faster at seeing and shifting on their own, so over time, the experience of doing "hard" things, pursuing scary big dreams, or making decisions just gets easier and easier for them.

If this sounds exciting to you, you might seek out an ontological coach trained in this coaching model. If you're low income, know that many of these coaches offer scholarships and pro bono coaching. To find a coach you vibe with, visit https://acecoachtraining.com/coaches/.

Create a Loving Partnership With Your Body

Regardless of how you treat your body, it is always loving you. It loves you unconditionally whether you do your physical therapy exercises every day or not. It will always be doing its best to restore equilibrium and help you heal fully. Even in the case of autoimmune diseases, in which the body attacks itself, it's not trying to destroy you—it's more that its efforts are misdirected. It might actually be trying too hard to protect you. It is still loving you and worthy of your love.

Learning to love your body, no matter what it's doing or what it looks like, is a crucial element of healing. As long as you're hating on your weak lungs or your muffin top, you're hating yourself. As much as we'd like to try, we cannot compartmentalize. You and your body have to be on the same team, and you have to cheer your body on when it's having a hard time.

Easier said than done, I know—especially when you grow up in an environment that teaches you to hate your body and that it's something to hide and be ashamed of. And if you're someone with marginalized identities, you might have gotten even more programming about how your body is too big, too skinny, too dark, too pale, too weird, too queer, too disabled, or worse. But, just like with the ideas we have about work, money, and achievement, you can choose to dismantle your structures of knowing about what a body is supposed to look like or what it's supposed to do. And it doesn't have to be a perfect "I-love-all-of-myself-all-the-time" kind of thing.

You can, and I suggest you do, bring some lightness to the practice of loving your body. Most of us have parts of our bodies that we're less than pleased with, and in the same way you might get annoyed at a romantic or business partner, you might be annoyed with your hair, or ankle, or whatever. So the question to ask yourself is, are you willing to be real and loving at the same time? Like, "Hey, Body. I'm annoyed that you don't have the energy for us to go Mohammed's birthday party, but I love you, you're sexy as hell, we're gonna get a medal for how well we rest tonight." Call me bananas, but I actually say things like that out loud to myself in the mirror.

When you love your body, you are more present to it, and you can actually give it what it needs. This runs counter to what a lot of us learn growing up, which is to treat symptoms and keep going. In other words, ignore your body. Headache? Take an aspirin. Got a cold? Take cold suppressants and go to work.

I operated that way for a long time. I developed a pretty detrimental caffeine addiction. With enough coffee I couldn't feel how tired and in pain I actually was, and it became a kind of antidepressant. For a while my dependency was so pronounced that I would start to cry on my way to work until my coffee kicked in and I felt closer to "normal" again. As you can imagine, with all that coffee, I wasn't very good at sleeping, so I also experimented with all kinds of sleeping aids, none of which were particularly good for me. I eventually quit caffeine so I could learn to listen to my body, and it was one of the best things I did for my healing.[99]

Tommy Rosen, who is nationally known for teaching yoga as a tool for addiction recovery, said in a workshop I attended that everyone should quit caffeine. He swore it would change our lives. It took me another year to follow his advice but, at least in my case, he was 100% right. Getting myself off caffeine forced me to be present with my body in a way that allowed me to actually hear it, honor it, and make some really helpful changes.

There's no one way to get to ultimate body love if that's even a thing. Learning to love and accept the body takes time and some trial and error. It will also be a longer, more arduous journey for some than it

---

99 Today I use caffeine in small doses but I was caffeine-free for nearly four years.

will be for others given your body type, trauma, and identities, but I believe it is possible for everyone to build a loving partnership with their body.

If that's something you want to do, there are some great body-love resources out there. You can find a wealth of inspiration by searching #bodypositivity on Instagram. I love the work of Elizabeth Cooper, who has all kinds of great reading and resources on her Queer Body Love website[100], and I really enjoy following Sonya Renee Taylor, founder of The Body Is Not An Apology, "a digital media and education company promoting radical self-love and body empowerment as the foundational tool for social justice and global transformation."[101]

If you're feeling like you'd love some extra help on this front, you might look for a therapist you like, especially if you have or think you might have an eating disorder or body dysmorphic disorder.[102] There are therapists who specialize in these conditions and body image in general. Psychology Today's website has a therapist search tool that allows you to filter by specialty and identity, for example a POC therapist who works on healing eating disorders.

If they are accessible to you, movement practices like yoga, dance, chi gong, tai chi, Alexander Technique, Nia, Feldenkrais, Afro-Flow Yoga, Qoya, Authentic Movement, and other others can do wonders in allowing you to feel like a boss in your body. Not only do these practices build bodily awareness, but they will teach you when you say "yes" and "no" to certain movements in accordance with your body's ability on any given day.

In a yoga studio you can usually pick out the seasoned practitioners based on how much they modify and what they choose *not* to do. The seasoned practitioner knows what's supportive and not supportive for

100 "Queer Body Love," accessed February 2, 2023, https://www.elizabethjcooper.com/.

101 "About," Sonya Renee Taylor, accessed February 2, 2023, https://www.sonyareneetaylor.com/about.

102 "Body Dysmorphic Disorder (BDD): Anxiety And," Body Dysmorphic Disorder (BDD) | Anxiety and, accessed February 2, 2023, https://adaa.org/understanding-anxiety/related-illnesses/other-related-conditions/body-dysmorphic-disorder-bdd.

their body moment to moment. They understand that one day they might be able to do a fancy balancing pose, but the next day it might be better to spend more time in child's pose. The reason so many people say yoga saved or healed them is because it's a widely accessible pathway to embodiment—that is, feeling present in your body and connected to its needs and desires. Most Americans are walking around disconnected from their bodies most of the time, so when they experience embodiment in an hour-long dance or yoga class for the first time, it can feel truly life changing.

If you're in a place where you feel extra disconnected from your body right now, or even like you're in an antagonistic relationship with it, I recommend starting slowly. Before you sign up for a class, try some YouTube videos or simply move to music in a room by yourself, or with a friend, and see how it goes. Baby steps are your friend.

Yoga has been one of *my* greatest tools in learning to be in partnership with my body, but I dislike that "do yoga" has culturally become a cure-all for every ailment in this country. That's as broad and vague as telling someone that reading will make them smarter. Read what? Fiction? Self-help? Erotica? Just "doing yoga" might not achieve the desired result of increased embodiment.

Plus, the impact of yoga, on both the body and mind, ranges tremendously from hot power yoga, which is very athletic, to restorative yoga, which involves lying on pillows and blankets in different positions for long periods of time. Restorative is super gentle, whereas hot power vinyasa, if not practiced with care, can really mess up your body.[103] I do believe that everyone can gain some benefit from yoga, no matter how disabled or autonomically dysfunctional.

---

103 It's my opinion that a lot of hot power yoga is taught at a speed that is too fast for many folks, especially beginner yogis, to practice safely. That said, every teacher is different and if you can tolerate the heat, hot yoga can be super healing, especially for folks with Lyme who need to detox as much as possible. I tend to avoid Baptiste and Bikram-informed classes and look for studios that offer slow-moving hot yoga. It's a good practice to call or email the studio and ask about the speed and intensity of their classes and how classes differ from teacher to teacher and see what sounds good to you.

But I'm speaking about all eight limbs of yoga, of which asana, the physical practice, is just one. Yoga is a practice that must be approached thoughtfully, especially given the identity crisis that yoga in the West is currently undergoing. Not only has the practice been warped by capitalism and changed through the process of cultural appropriation, but we are becoming increasingly aware of how it's been used as a vehicle for sexual violence in certain yoga lineages, most famously by Ashtanga founder Krishna Pathabi Jois.[104]

My advice is to do your research on the studio, teachers, and types of yoga you're interested in. Ask enough questions to discern whether a certain practice feels aligned for you. Look for studios and teachers that make you feel comfortable and able to ask questions. Also, yoga is only one access point to experience freedom in your body. I have, at times, stopped doing and teaching yoga in favor of less rigid and more expansive practices like dance and Authentic Movement. My most favorite movement practice is Afro Flow Yoga, a hybrid yoga and Afro-Caribbean dance community that I've been privileged to practice with for many years.

I've seen dance in particular help so many spoonies heal. I've also had a lot of folks tell me that they can't dance anymore or feel embarrassed to get back into it after taking time off. It's good to remember that there are many kinds of dance, and some dance communities are especially welcoming to people with differing physical abilities. If you're craving movement and looking for new ways to do it, seek out classes, clubs, studios, leagues, and teams for folks with different abilities and different body types.

If you're a big-bodied person, you might look for movement practitioners who identify as practitioners of Healthy At Every Size (HAES). In Somerville, Massachusetts, a yoga teacher named Rachel Estapa

---

104 Canadian yoga researcher Matthew Remski has spoken and written extensively about Jois, and abuse in yoga and Buddhist communities more broadly. He has proposed a framework for how we can begin to heal what's been done and prevent future abuse. "Yoga, Writing & Inquiry," Matthew Remski, January 2, 2021, http://matthewremski.com/wordpress/.

founded More to Love Yoga, yoga specifically tailored for plus-size folks. In the Boston-area there are also queer, trans, and POC-specific yoga and movement classes. As I mentioned before, one of my clients is part of a dance team in Boston specifically for people with disabilities, and another client is a proud member of a local adaptive rock-climbing team. If movement of any kind is out of the question right now, visualize yourself dancing or moving, maybe along with some music, and notice what it does for your mood and your relationship with your body.

On your quest to develop a loving partnership with your body, allow yourself to try a few different paths. If you hate the first thing you try, it doesn't mean you failed. You may love the next thing! And just like with romantic relationships, there will be ups and downs. You will question your body just like you'd question a lover. It will take a while to build trust. That's all normal. Keep breathing, keep listening, keep being curious, and remember that your body already loves you unconditionally and is standing by, patiently waiting for you to do the same.

Practice Joy and Pleasure

"My joy takes nothing from you."
—Frazey Ford

One of the ways you can begin to love your body, even if it's challenging mentally, is to explore and experience the things that make you feel pleasure. I covered this a bit in Section 1 but want to explain more just how integral pleasure has been in my healing journey. I believe cultivating joy and pleasure is essential to both personal healing and collective liberation.

For additional inspiration on the connection between reclaiming pleasure and dismantling systems of oppression, I highly recommend reading Naomi Ortiz' *Sustaining Spirit: Self Care for Social Justice* and adrienne maree brown's *Pleasure Activism: The Politics of Feeling Good.*

In recent history, the dominant cultural narrative around pleasure has been that pleasure is something that costs money and it's something that you give yourself as a reward. So, if you're broke and not terribly "productive" in a normative sense, then you might feel like you don't deserve to experience pleasure. Obviously, that is not the truth, but a lot of us have been programmed to think that way and we deny ourselves joy as a result. We are also programmed to believe that pursuing our own joy is selfish, and that we should be dedicated to the joy of others. A lot of us, especially folks socialized as women, find it much easier to bake a cake for a friend than bake one for ourselves. But our joy and pleasure are not a threat to others and, unless we have an especially sick mind, we do not experience joy at the expense of others.

Joy is medicine because it helps us feel alive and stay connected to the joy of *being* alive, which in turn makes us more resilient. We need that joyful resiliency both to stay on the healing path and the justice path when things get hard. As I mentioned in the introduction, I spent years not excited to be alive and even now, I occasionally have moments when I wonder why it's important to be alive. I also still catch myself tempering my joy sometimes, or wondering if it's okay to pursue or even just feel joy when so many people are suffering. This is really normal. So, if this joy feels hard for you, all is well. You can grow into it.

Joy, by definition, is the feeling of pleasure. Pleasure, by definition, is the feeling of satisfaction. Both joy and pleasure include the feeling of happiness. So, I will talk about all three in concert. Getting a break from physical symptoms, as I did in 2019, gave me the space to see just how much I had limited my own pleasure. And while it would be easy to blame capitalism, the patriarchy, my family of origin, or the community I grew up in for this, at the end of the day, I see now how much I robbed myself of my own happiness and why, at the time, it felt like the right thing to do.

For years, when I was at my sickest, I worried that if I spent energy, time, or money on my own pleasure, it would come back later to bite me in the ass. Like a lot of spoonies, my scarcity mindset ruled my life, in the worst way. I denied myself so many things I love, like art and other things that brought me joy. I felt like I needed to hoard my precious resources—particularly money, time, and energy—because I never knew when they'd run out. My physical energy was unpredictable, and I felt like I had to save all my money for medicine. My number one biggest worry, especially after I became a business owner, was that I wouldn't do the right thing, I wouldn't make enough money, and I would end up starving, in pain, alone, and unhoused. And the thought of living on the street as a sick person felt especially stressful.

That story and the way it lived in my nervous system robbed me of a lot of life's pleasures for a long time. It's taken a lot of support, healing work, and personal resolve to shift it. The story didn't shift in a big way until I allowed myself to grieve all that I didn't allow myself to have or feel. I didn't let myself feel my pain, I didn't let people love me, and I didn't value my own pleasure.

One of the most painful things I denied myself was my love of art, writing, and other forms of artistic expression. I forgot, for almost a decade, how much I loved writing. Years ago, my first therapist said something off handedly about art and I burst into tears. I felt so estranged from art, both making it and being around it, and I didn't even realize how much that had hurt my soul.

Growing up going to high school in Virginia, I'd go to D.C. any chance I could get, tool around the Hirshhorn Museum, use my high school ID to get into the Corcoran Gallery, which I loved so much. I felt, and still feel at peace around a lot of art, even with art I don't understand.

It's taken a few years and a lot of practice to come back to art appreciation and then art-making. I have learned that making the work isn't even as important as simply letting the ideas in. Engaging with the voice that says "there's no time to make that," or "what's the point?" and doing something anyway is a growth edge for me, and oh so sweet when I follow through.

It's historically felt challenging to make for the sake of making, understanding that even if I draw 3,000 shitty pictures that no one sees, that I burn at my altar or leave in the recycling, it will do some good for me. In moments when I *have* shared my art, my writing, or my voice, it has felt wonderful, freeing, empowering, and like a massive burden has been lifted off my shoulders. I've found pursuing joy and pleasure to be an endlessly rewarding self-love practice.

In general, when centering on pleasure, my healing has become an exercise in slowing down and savoring—savoring food, friendships, time to watch the seaweed sway in the water, the creative process, the space to surrender, and the time to cry when that is what I'm being called to do. At least in my experience, creation and joy, like healing, require surrender.

And in this culture, where there is so much competition for our attention, surrender is something we have to practice—like mindfulness, like brushing our teeth, like being kind. When I surrender, it makes space for newness to emerge: new words, new visions, new ideas for what I could be when I grow up. A yoga teacher buddy of mine once said that there's one long tube between your mouth and your asshole (her words, not mine) and yoga is about relaxing and opening the tube so things can move.

I find surrendering to be a similar process. When we finally relax and surrender, it allows for movement, ideas, feelings, and epiphanies to emerge. We let some of it go, and then we get to create with the remaining bits of sparkly glory.

I have seen this happen a few times in my life, and one instance in particular sticks out. In college, I had the great honor of being in a semester-long course with the legendary feminist artist Judy Chicago. I was given my own space in a gallery and a budget of $750 to create whatever I wanted. It was one of the hardest and most wonderful experiences I've ever had.

My piece made the whole room smell like beeswax. I had melted whole pounds of it, one brick at a time, in a microwave on the other side of the building. The beeswax covered paper-mâché, which covered chicken wire, which covered a wooden frame generously created for me by my carpenter ex-boyfriend. It made a big yellow blob on the gallery floor.

Over the beeswax mass, meant to look like snot, were piles of tissues, prescription bottles, pills, cigarette boxes, and Diet Coke cans. The joke at Vanderbilt was that all the women lived off cigarettes and Diet Coke. I ate, but I wasn't immune to the trends. Out of the yellow mass reached mannequin arms and legs wrapped in health insurance statements. Then there were things hanging from the ceiling. Fake flowers, a soccer cleat, an Amartya Sen book.

I was creating. I was creating so hard that I ended up ugly crying in the arms of Judy Chicago. I was especially sleep deprived, having stayed up past midnight for several weeks working on my sculpture. I honestly don't remember if Judy was giving me praise or criticism, but she came to check-in on my work one day and whatever she said struck something tender in me. I collapsed into a pile of dry heaving and tears.

Without missing a beat, the well-known ruthless critic wrapped me in her arms and held me. She surprised me with her kindness and tenderness, and yet I was surely not the first artist to lose my shit in her presence and not the first artist to feel all the feels of surrendering to the most painful parts of artmaking. She was no stranger to the shadow side of the creative process and her confidence in my okay-ness really stuck with me.

With renewed confidence, I stayed up late many more nights, working on the sculpture by myself, happy that I could listen to my favorite music. One night a friend came to visit and we snuck onto the roof to smoke pot. It felt so naughty, doing something so clearly unsafe, on the roof of an academic building. But I didn't care any-more. I'd settled into a kind of sweet, I-don't-give-any-fucks delirium. Nothing was more important than this piece, and I was on a deadline. I showed up to my other classes when I was supposed to but I wasn't really present. I was focused. Focused on finishing this piece that expressed everything I hadn't said, everything I didn't share about my own complexities, coping mechanisms, and how freakin' hard it felt to be chronically ill at age 21. At the opening of the art show, so many people looked at me in awe. "I had no idea," floated towards my ears too many times to count.

The Nashville Scene ran a picture of my piece, my sculpture as big as a car, and the objects that hung above it—representing everything I felt I couldn't have. Of all the amazing art in that exhibit, some made by capital "P" professional artists, it was my piece that made it in the paper. I couldn't believe it, but also I could. I had never felt so at home, at ease, in the flow.

When I completed the piece, I felt wave after wave of relief, like multiple orgasms, given without any expectation of reciprocity. It was sweetness, peace, and the best kind of exhaustion. I felt spent. It wasn't just the energy of successfully illuminating invisible illness that made it so magical, but also hanging out with other artists, healing from a breakup with a man I thought I'd marry and learning how to be with early 20's angst. It felt like God was giving me a taste of what I was capable of. I loved who I was making this art.

I didn't even mind that we had to destroy the piece at the end. It was necessary to get it out the door. I remember expressing gratitude to the six black trash bags that contained all of my creation. I told them, "Thank you. Thank you for everything you gave me." It felt like the best kind of breakup. I'll remember it fondly, but it was also okay if we never saw each other again.

When I think about everything I've done in service of healing myself, saying "yes" to what brings me pleasure has always given me the most bang for my buck. Continuing to say "yes" to myself has been a sort of transference of energy away from throwing myself under the bus, and towards self-love. I've also, as you might imagine, been a lot happier. Engaging with things that bring me joy has helped heal the "I don't want to be here" borderline suicidal feelings that used to be a big part of my daily experience. Saying "yes" to what I love and doing more of it has also helped me get clearer about who I am in the world, and why I'm here, my raison d'etre. Writing this book is an example of that. It was a way to reclaim my identity as a writer. I took voice lessons to claim my identity as a singer, and I committed to a regular self-pleasure practice as a way to claim my identity as a sexual, pleasure-oriented being. And just to top it all off, I'll add that saying "yes" to my own pleasure simply fills me up and gives me more energy to be present for and support other people, which in turn, gives me more pleasure. It's kind of the best.

Reflection Questions:
- What pleasure have you denied yourself, while healing or otherwise?
- What are you missing and craving?
- What kind of pleasure would you love to experience (more of) in your life?
- What might be different in your life or your healing if you were regularly experiencing pleasure? How would it feel, in your body? In your soul?

Say "No" to Others and "Yes" to Yourself

"Boundaries are the distance at which I can love you and me simultaneously."

—Prentis Hemphill

Being clear on what you give your energy to is an important and sometimes challenging aspect of self-love practice. Someone told me once that surviving a chronic illness was like getting a PhD in being alive. What they meant was that when you're always unwell, in pain, and/or operating with limited energy, you learn pretty quickly what's really important and what's not. You no longer have time for bullshit—other people's or your own. You give way fewer fucks about what other people think because you simply do not have the energy for it. It also becomes easier to laser in on what you do want to spend your energy on.

Because of this stripping away of the bullshit, the healing process can be a sort of fast track to living life with a lot more ease and clarity. You're no longer able to engage with the world at the level that many people do, caught up in the drama. But getting to this point takes a lot of self-love, telling the truth, and potentially setting boundaries for yourself and people in your life.

I work primarily with entrepreneurs, people with health challenges, and people in social change circles—folks who all share some or a lot of my experience. What I see again and again is that a lot of our kind struggle to say "no" to things, even when it's very clearly in our self-interest to do so. We have trouble saying "no" to social engagements, family support asks, volunteer opportunities, political actions and more because we want so badly to contribute.

Sometimes, because there are things about us that make us uncomfortable, we distract ourselves from ourselves by supporting other people. We channel all our energy into supporting others so we don't have to look and see what's really going on inside of us. It's normal, and nothing to be ashamed of, but worth noticing if this is part of your pattern.

To do anything big in your life, like heal from a complex illness, start a business, write a book, or get a new job you love, you need to devote a decent amount of regular, focused energy and attention to that process. It requires at least some amount of solo time and energy conservation, things that can really seem out of reach when we're always attending to the needs of others.

I've seen even very enlightened people who have done lots of self-growth work struggle to make time for themselves and their own projects. It's so normal to want to be helpful and useful, but if we overdo it, we hinder ourselves from doing what's ours to do. I can't tell you how many folks have come to me for coaching saying things like, "I am really good at supporting other people with their projects but I can't seem to focus on my own."

It's understood in Traditional Chinese Medicine that energy follows focus. If you are always focused on others, that is where your energy will go. It is useful to learn how to gracefully say "no" in service of protecting your time, and it is just as important to learn how to say "yes" to yourself and what's important to you. To do that you have to be really clear about what you want to be focused on, and what you're willing to do to make it happen.

Once you're clear on that, it's easier to see where and when you're spending time on things that aren't supporting your goals. If you see that you have trouble saying "no" to things that you don't really want to do, or that aren't in your best interest, your first step is to get a sense of what makes you say "yes" to them.

Some typical reasons why we do things we don't actually want to do:
- You don't want to disappoint anyone
- You want to be liked

- You avoid conflict
- You feel like saying "no" means you're being selfish

All of those reasons are normal. Humans want to be liked and want to continue to be included in the human herd. Make a point to observe when you feel uncomfortable about responding to a request. What is the root of that discomfort? What is the inner tension about?

You must also get crystal clear on what's most important to you in your life right now, or what you actually want to say "yes" to. If you've written a healing vision statement, that will be a great guiding document for you. You might also already have goals from the Support Dream Team section, but if not, start by making a list of three things that you really want to accomplish and three values that you want to put into practice in the next three to six months. Keep the list handy, like on your phone or on your wall so you can refer to it easily.

The list might look like:

Things to Accomplish by *Month, Date, Year (three months from now)*
- Find and make an appointment with a new chiropractor
- Launch Etsy page to sell my art
- Take my little brother to a baseball game

Intentions to demonstrate in scoring these goals:
- Taking good care of my body
- Attracting more money into my life
- Being a loving family member

This list can be a barometer for you to use when making decisions about how you're spending your time and energy. You'll want to make the list relevant to the context(s) in which you struggle the most to say "no." If you have a job and really struggle with saying "no" at work, for example, choose goals and values that will require you to stand up for yourself at work. Let's look at how to put this into practice.

When someone asks you to do something, you can consult your list and ask yourself, "Will this support me in doing what's on the list?" If not, you might feel a little better about saying no simply because you're clear on *why* you're saying "no." And if you do say "no," with clarity, you get to celebrate the small, sweet act of self-love you gifted yourself.

When someone asks you to do something, practice pausing before you respond. If possible, consult your list, but at the very least, before you give someone an answer, practice taking a deep breath and asking yourself, "Do I really want to do this?" You could also ask,

"Will this bring me joy?"

"Will this help me do what I'm trying to do right now?" or simply "Will this be fun?"

Of course, you will likely have to do some things that don't bring you joy, especially in the context of family or work. So, at work, a better question might be, "Do I really have the capacity to take this on right now?" With family, you might ask if there's a way you can meet the request on terms that work a little better for you. Whenever possible, ask the person requesting if you can think about it and get back to them.

This is a helpful practice anyway, because it can give you time to check your calendar, consult your priority list, and gather any other information that could help you make a more informed decision. Asking if you can get back to someone is an especially good practice if you say "yes" a lot and then bail on things because you weren't clear on your available time, energy, and interest.

The more you practice taking the time to consider whether you want to say "yes," the more you will reduce the overwhelm and scheduling conflicts that lead to last-minute bailing. It will also save you a lot of emotional energy. At first it will seem like you're saying "no" a lot, but the more you practice, the easier it will be to say "no" and "yes" with ease. As you get better and better at saying "no," and worry less about disappointing others, your energy—emotional and physical—gets freed up in a big way.

No longer wracked with guilt, you feel lighter, and life becomes more spacious. With more space, you'll begin to see more clearly what you need to do for the mental and spiritual aspects of your healing. When you're worrying about what other people think and need all the time, the worry is a brilliant distraction from yourself and what *you* need. Without distraction, you are left with just yourself and the truth, and that can be terrifying, especially at first.

But remember, you have a lot of tools to get through the scary times, like calling in support from friends or professionals, your mindfulness practice, and the intuitive practices outlined in Strengthen Your Intuition.

Once you let go of other people's wants and needs a little and spend more time observing and listening to yourself, it can create a kind of yellow brick road effect. One way to think about illness is that it's a sort of rite of passage, a heroine's journey you have to say "yes" to in order to clearly see your gifts and what you have to contribute to the world.

The more you listen to what's coming up in you, and the more you say "yes" to those things and follow the sparks that emerge, the more you will be living from your healing vision. So, as you begin to tune into yourself more, you want to be curious about what you're feeling called to do. In my case it was singing, writing, and moving out of the city.

For my friend and very gifted healer Emily Royce, it was dancing, and specifically traveling to learn different kinds of dance and healing modalities. Her dance journey led her to tantra, which led her to becoming a sexological bodyworker. This was not necessarily what she imagined for herself when she first said "yes" to the longing to dance. For other folks the call might be teaching mathematics or getting into animal husbandry. You might have an inkling of what it is already, you might not. That's part of the adventure!

In an episode of the podcast *Quality of Being*, host Jacob Farris and guest Rochelle Schiek drop some serious wisdom about figuring out your calling.[105] Rochelle points out that if you have no idea, it's probably because you're exhausted. Jacob shares that the best way to get clues about your calling is simply to follow your interests and see where they lead you. So, if you're in the "I don't know what my calling is" camp, rest more and stay curious. It's also not uncommon for spoonies to be so wrapped up in self-maintenance that it's hard to see anything beyond it. If that resonates, I want to encourage you to look beyond the self-care work you're doing and ask what would really bring you joy. You'll want to practice being open and non-judgmental, because the things that emerge may seem impossible at first. Write them down and let them marinate. You don't have to act on anything right away. Here are some questions to guide your inquiry and help you clarify what you want to be saying "yes" to in your life. You could consult your intuition on these questions, write about them, talk to a trusted friend—whatever feels useful to you:

- What is really important to me right now?
- What would bring me joy?
- What do I need to heal?
- What have I been daydreaming about?
- What would bring me so much joy that it scares me a little to think about actually doing it?
- If everything was possible and there was no possibility of failure, what would I do next?
- What are the dreams I haven't pursued yet?
- What hobbies and interests got left behind when I got sick, or simply as life happened?

---

105 Jacob Farris, interview with Rochelle Schiek, Quality of Being, podcast audio, June 18, 2019, https://qualityof-beingpodcast.com/2019/06/18/podcast-002-rochelle-schieck/.

Those dark corners of your being are where you're going to find the keys to unlock your healing. You'll want to really give yourself space to consider these questions. That could look like going on a trip somewhere and really getting deep with yourself, but it could also be as simple as taking twenty minutes a day to meditate or write on these questions. You may have heard of the questions, attributed to Indigenous shamans on Turtle Island, "When was the last time you sang? When was the last time you danced? When was the last time you told your story?" I have seen many a spoonie heal through dance, song, and storytelling.

If you're feeling at a loss about what you really want to say "yes" to, start with self-expression. You can't go wrong. While modern medicine often doesn't encourage it, self-expression has always been an essential part of processing grief and trauma, whether it's related to chronic illness or not. In my case, coming back to writing, singing, and painting has been hugely beneficial to my healing. If self-expression scares you, remember that it is a contribution. It educates and inspires others, and helps people feel more connected and less alone with their experience.

When I decided to really kick my self-love game up a notch in 2017, I did so by saying yes to things that had been on my heart for a long time, and a lot of it was rooted in self-expression. I took voice lessons. I moved to a small town with lots of opportunities to play outside. I started a book club. I went to yoga class 4-5 times a week for a large chunk of the year.[106] I let myself rest without feeling bad about it. I joined a writing group and wrote fiction and poetry for the first time in 15 years. Early in 2018, I joined a choir and sang in front of people for the first time ever.

Doing those things took a little sacrifice. I chose not to move in with my partner at the time, and in fact I moved two hours away from him. The move was also financially draining since I had not planned

---

106 This was financially possible because I had a work-study position at my local studio. If you have the spoons to volunteer a little time, work-study positions are a great way to get free yoga, dance, and other forms of healing that might otherwise feel cost-prohibitive if you're presently low-income.

for it. I could have worked more to make up for it, but I saw that pursuing the things that really fed me were going to help me more in my healing. And they did. Moving out of the city for a year, giving myself permission to say "no" to anything that didn't sound fun, and reclaiming my identity as an artist were three of the best things I did for my healing.

I hope that these self-love practices spark something in you that supports you in your journey. There are many ways to love yourself. You have to find what really feels like love to you. It's helpful to dedicate time to it and make at least part of your self-love practice body based. When we are fully in our bodies, we are more present to ourselves and our desires, our humanity, the earth, and the divine. Taking the time to love yourself from the inside out is a contribution to our collective liberation. When you love yourself, you're able to contribute what's yours from that place of wholeness and show up fully present for others with a truly open heart.

Reflection Questions:
- What comes up for you about loving yourself?
- Where does it feel easy vs. more challenging?
- How would you like to practice loving yourself and your body?

Record your answers in your healing journal.

Surrender

We've gone through a lot of practices, exercises, and healing modalities you can explore for your journey. Before wrapping things up, it feels important to say more about something perhaps less tangible but no less critical on the healing path: surrender. In case this is something that you struggle with, I hope that reading about my experience gives you permission to surrender even a little bit more.

One lesson my body continues to teach me over and over again is that healing requires time, space, and surrendering to what is. We need to make space for the body to do what it needs to do, even if it's not pretty, even if we don't want to. Your body might need to violently expel a toxin from both ends of you, it might need to cry for six months, or it might need to lie very still for most or all of the day for what feels like a very long time.

We can try to fight it, but surrendering to what the body needs will be more fruitful. Bulldozing the body and pushing through typically doesn't end well. Not everyone has the option to give the body what it needs but I encourage you to do everything you can—ask for help, apply for disability, trade favors with your neighbors, etc.—to give yourself what you need in order to surrender to your healing, even just a little bit.

In the course of my healing journey, I've learned that my body likes a lot of space to lie still, a lot of space to cry, and a lot of time to sleep. Even when I have felt close to 100% well for months at a time, my body's primary way of processing a head cold, grief, or a great healing session is nap time. I also find that I still need to make space for crying, and feeling emotions in general, which is something I didn't allow myself for a long time.

I didn't realize until pretty late in my healing journey how much emotional repression, and a related unwillingness to let people love me, stoked and reinforced my illness. I held tight and fast to a few close friendships and wasn't really ever vulnerable unless someone explicitly created the space for it. And even then, I resisted being vulnerable with others. I don't blame my parents for this, because I think it's simply a generational and cultural thing, but I got the message pretty early on that expressing feelings wasn't really okay in our household.

Being tough and flexible were highly valued, and the coaches and teachers I had growing up reinforced those values. I learned as a young rider, for example, that if you fell off a horse, the most important thing was to get up and back in the saddle no matter what.

When I was little, my dad used to ask, rhetorically, "You need a cork for that whine?" I always thought it was funny, and it kind of is, but I recently realized that it reinforced this understanding I had that I was supposed to just "be good"—not cry, not complain, not cause problems. I think it's normal for parents to want that of their children, especially my dad's generation.

From what I understand, I was quite verbose as a child, and it probably got old. When my brother came along and became the more energy-intensive child, my ability to "be good" and fade into the background had its benefits. Most of the time I was able to avoid getting in trouble myself. But it was also lonely. I spent a lot of time crying by myself, or with the animals in my life.

I felt deeply connected to animals because they still loved me in my messiness. In high school I joked with friends that I was going to take my dog to prom because he was really the being I most loved spending time with. When I left home for college, I didn't have access to animals in the same way, and I lost that source of acceptance and unconditional love. I felt really alone with my feelings.

That carried into adulthood and led to a habit of isolating myself when I had a lot to feel. I felt a lot of shame, and like I shouldn't have so much to cry about. I bottled things up, and when I inevitably burst, crying became a big exhausting ordeal. Eventually I got myself into therapy and my lovely therapist said, "If all you do is come to my office once a week and cry for an hour, that's great."

She said that at a time when I cried often and I worried that the crying might never stop. After years of holding in all my pain, sadness, and frustration, my body couldn't hold it anymore. In hindsight, it was probably a nervous system response to working a stressful job while living with lots of physical pain from an untreated widespread bacterial infection. At that point, I'd been sick and in pain for around eight years and didn't have a diagnosis that felt right or helpful. I'd spent eight years feeling like I had to hide my reality, suck it up, and show up as normal for other people.

It was eight years of wondering why a lot of things were harder for me than they were for my peers. Eight years of going from doctor to doctor looking for support that didn't seem to be available. Eight years of wondering if it was my fault and if I just tried hard enough to be strong, meditate, and to eat the right things, maybe I would be free in my body like everyone around me.

So, you know, there were a few things to cry about. I don't remember exactly how long the crying time lasted. It was probably three or four months, but it felt like an eternity. It was really lonely because I didn't want anyone to see me cry. As I mentioned before, I'd sit on my bed, phone in hand, desperately wanting to call my best friends from college, the ones who I knew would love me no matter what, but I felt so much shame.

For years after the crying time ended, I was afraid to cry. I worried that if I let myself cry even a little, it might again turn into months of crying. And such regular crying was inconvenient. It made it hard to work and show up the way I was supposed to, especially after starting my own coaching practice. I felt like I had to show up for my clients. I had to be the one who had my shit together.

It was, and sometimes still is, really difficult to believe that anyone, even the folks I feel safest with, actually want to be witness to my snotty, ugly cries. In the last year or so, I have been trying to be more vulnerable about it, and with good results. Peer counseling has been enormously helpful for this process. But before I found that, I went through another crying time after one of my favorite healers died unexpectedly in February 2019.

Her passing cracked open a huge well of grief that I didn't even know was there. With a greater understanding of how important it is for physical health to feel and process emotions, I really let the feelings and the tears come this time. Since I was running my own business, I had the privilege of moving my appointments around when I needed to feel the feels. I also took a lot of time to just be. I learned of my healer's passing during a month-long dog-sitting gig in a rural area. I had everything I needed at the house and could go days without seeing anyone if I didn't want to. I did a lot of sitting on the couch, just letting myself cry, with the dog curled up next to me.

Sometimes I just sat and stared out the window. In the months after, I went through a long, slow breakup and the crying continued. It took more than three months to cry out all that was there but I can tell you that I felt like a million bucks when it was over. I also let some of my friends see me cry. I talked to them about what I was experiencing and let them hold me, and I was excited to learn that they still wanted to be friends with me afterwards.

Here is something that I wrote in a writing salon that May, after a few months of crying nearly daily:

This is MY block to bust through. My voice feels stifled from deep within. I have pushed it down for so many years and it feels unsafe to express. I feel sad just writing about it. I have been coming undone for so long now. I am tired of this part of healing. Back in November, a psychic told me that I was entering a unique time and that I was particularly fragile, but not in a bad way. She said there were cracks in me that could allow me to access my core. If I chose to dive into those cracks, I could experience deep healing. If I chose not to, I could miss the window and there was no telling when it would come back.

As a Capricorn and a Three on the Enneagram, I have approached my healing with great fervor and dedication, determined and driven, sometimes to a fault. But given the opportunity to up-level my healing, how could I say "no?" Sure I was scared, but I was willing. So I have dragged myself through the pain of the last six months, head down and heart open, trying to love every part of myself that is scarred, cracked, ticklish, and terrified. If this period of time were an epochal economic event, I would name it The Great Unraveling.

One of my goals for 2019 was to let myself cry without judgment. When I took a yearlong sabbatical from the city and took up residence in the tiny Hilltown of Shelburne Falls, home to the glacial potholes, which some call a healing vortex, two of my best friends were men around 60 who cried at the drop of a hat. Brook talked openly about how much he cried, and we cried together over coffee when he spoke of his late mother Blanca, and the way she rolled up the carpet just before people came over for the legendary parties she threw, so there was plenty of room for dancing. Chris cries when he talks about the beauty of the Universe. A baby, a perfect dandelion, any touch of God's hand can bring tears to his eyes. I thought to myself, these guys have a few decades on me. They know some shit. If they cry this much and I can still love them so much, I can let myself cry too.

The crying has been a river running through the various stages of the Great Unraveling and with it has come a renaissance of my voice, literally and otherwise. I am letting go of the things that do not serve me, shedding different parts of my ego, and surrendering to the unknown. I am learning how to be irresponsible. For the first time in my life I have a few grand on a credit card and no plan for how to pay it off. The card is interest free for 15 months but that's not the point.

In a recent session with my friend and healing mentor Ishita, I screamed for the first time in my life. It felt amazing. I got a glimpse of my power, and the singer I want to be in the world. Since high school I have had a sense that I was a soul singer in a past life. That could explain the deep pain of non-expression, my illness, the loneliness, everything. I am an artist. I am an artist. I am a fucking artist. Writing that makes me cry because it is so true and yet I have suppressed it so thoroughly and effectively. Why is it so hard to express?

It's easy to blame my family, our dynamic, our culture, whatever, but in the end I did it. I told myself I couldn't possibly make music or art. I told myself I had to change the world. I told myself I had to do something serious.

Little body, I love you so much and I'm sorry. Please forgive me.

I repeat the Hawaiian prayer whenever I remember. "I love you. I'm sorry. Please forgive me."

On paper, the last six months look so hard—a marriage proposal I didn't want, the end of a relationship I loved more than any I'd had before, the loss of a healer, teacher, and guide, moving twice, my invincible dad getting sick with the same diseases that have hung out in my shadow for twenty years, and then sitting in the ER with a friend who can't speak, asking the doctor the same question four different ways to see if we'd get another answer, and the way that ER experience brought up years and years of pain still inside me from doctors saying "no" "I can't" "I'm sorry." And here I am—still standing, still okay.

I will be heard. I will be seen. I'm sure it will continue to feel like a battle and a slog but the promise of joy is so sweet, like a million cherry pies made with the best ingredients: butter and love. If it requires me to destroy every last atom of my sense of self, I am willing.

Out of that big crying time I experienced the greatest uptick in my physical health yet. I felt so good for almost a year, it seemed offensive to people with chronic illness to say that I still had one. I felt like I could do almost anything I wanted, except eat pizza and ice cream—and since I hadn't done those things in years, I knew I could survive without them. The undercurrent of everything that got me to that point in my healing was a willingness to love myself and give myself the space to cry without judgment and without trying to make it stop. It was surprisingly challenging at times but allowing myself to honor and make space for whatever emotions and needs come up has yielded huge rewards.

Reflection Questions:
- How do you feel about the word "surrender?"
- How easy or hard is it for you to give yourself what you need?
- Do you see opportunities to make your healing a little more spacious?
- How can you support yourself to feel the feels?

Record your reflections in your healing journal.

Honoring Our Collective Heart

Hopefully throughout these chapters you have found some sweet nuggets to support you in your healing. And maybe you now also see how being on the healing path is essential to our collective liberation. Your rebellious healing is a contribution.

While we could write a never-ending list of all the things that are wrong with the United States of America in this time, there are just as many opportunities for change, redemption, and new paradigms. We can only heal the white supremacist, racial capitalist, patriarchal, and other oppressive kyriarchal constructs that live within us and our society by dreaming new possibilities into being.

Dreaming doesn't happen as easily, or at all, when you are completely exhausted, depleted, and beat down. Dreaming is made possible by being on the healing path. This is how the healing path and the justice path become one. Each small shift and healing victory makes space for new possibilities in our own lives and for the collective. The more resourced we are, the more capacity we have to light up our own lives and contribute to our communities.

Make sure dreaming is part of your practice and do it with others whenever you can. If dreaming feels challenging now, know that it will get easier as you progress in your healing. Remember you are not alone in your suffering, and do what you can to lean into love, care, and connection. Practice being in right relationship with your body, the Earth, the divine, your ancestors, and your community. At this time, that is one of the most anti-capitalist, anti-oppressive actions you can practice.

When you find yourself in positions of power, practice centering disabled, Black, Indigenous, queer, and trans voices and needs.

Remember that resourcing and prioritizing the most marginalized helps us all be more free. No matter your identity, find ways to share your own story too. It will help others feel seen, heard and connected.

As your healing unfolds, remember to approach it with lightness and be gentle with yourself. The healing path never ends, so look out for opportunities to bring in joy and pleasure along the way. There will always be more to heal, and there will always be another horizon to explore. There's no rush, and you can slow it all the way down when you want to. If you need a break from healing, that's okay. It will be waiting for you when you're ready to come back to it.

You also get to choose who joins you on the journey and when. You are the captain, and you get to make healing whatever you want it to be. If you're someone who does political work and you choose to take a break from that, trust that healing can be your political work, and you'll know when it's time to engage again. The way you make change in the world and serve your community may shift.

Resist the urge to judge or compare yourself and remember that the best thing you can do, for yourself and the collective, is honor your body, honor your gifts, and keep bringing people into what you're up to. Community. Community. Community. That is how we achieve collective liberation. So, take good care and have some fun, okay?

Final Reflection Questions:
- How might you create and sustain a dreaming practice, solo or with others?
- Flip back through your healing journal. What stands out to you as being particularly useful? What has already shifted in your healing as a result of bringing more awareness to the mental, spiritual, and emotional aspects of healing?
- What have you learned? What do you still want to learn?
- How can you bring healing to your communities in service of justice and liberation?

GLOSSARY

Ableism - From the Center for Disability Rights, "Ableism is a set of beliefs or practices that devalue and discriminate against people with physical, intellectual, or psychiatric disabilities and often rests on the assumption that disabled people need to be 'fixed' in one form or the other."[107]

Anti-oppression - The practice of actively opposing and changing oppressive dynamics at the interpersonal level and working to eradicate or change oppressive policies and systems.

Antiracist - From Ibram X. Kendi, "One who is supporting an antiracist policy through their actions or expressing an antiracist idea."[108]

BIPOC - This acronym stands for Black, Indigenous, and People of Color. I am using it to center the specific violence and injustices (past and present) against Black and Indigenous people in the United States, from enslavement and genocide up to today.

---

107 Leah Smith, "Center for Disability Rights," #Ableism – Center for Disability Rights, accessed January 12, 2023, https://cdrnys.org/blog/uncategorized/ableism/.
108 Ibram X. Kendi, How to Be an Antiracist (New York, NY: One World, 2019).

Capitalism - From Merriam-Webster, "an economic system character-ized by private or corporate ownership of capital goods, by investments that are determined by private decision, and by prices, production, and the distribution of goods that are determined mainly by competition in a free market." Capitalism as a system prioritizes perpetual growth. In *Debt: The First 5,000 Years*, David Graeber writes, "Capitalism is first and foremost the art of using money to get more money." I like this definition because it makes it clear that if you don't have money to begin with, e.g. if you are born into a low-income family, don't have inherited wealth in the form of home or land ownership, or you've spent all your savings on medicine and you can't work, it is very challenging for you to make money in a capitalist economy.

Cisgender - Denoting or relating to a person whose sense of personal identity and gender corresponds with the sex assigned to them at birth. (For example, a cis woman is someone who identifies as a woman and was assigned female at birth). Sometimes I will simply use "cis" as in "cis men" to differentiate from transgender, or simply trans men.

Collective liberation - United Students Against Sweatshops (USAS), which hosted the first grassroots organizing and anti-oppression train-ings I ever attended as a student activist, defines collective liberation like this:[109]

> Collective liberation means recognizing that all of our struggles are intimately connected, and that we must work together to create the kind of world we know is possible. We believe that every person is worthy of dignity and respect, and that within systems of oppression everyone suffers.

109USAS, "Collective Liberation," United Students Against Sweatshops, accessed January 13, 2023, https://web.archive.org/web/20140911171141/http://usas.org/about/collective-liberation/.

Collective liberation is not just a value, but an action. When we work together across the barriers kept in place to divide us, we strengthen our organizing. When combined, our diverse identities and experiences give us the tools to dismantle systems of economic and social oppression, and to create a world in which all people are seen as fully human.

Complex Trauma - Complex trauma occurs in response to repeated traumatic incidents that cause fear, terror, powerlessness, or helplessness over an extended period of time, like months or years. It is distinct from acute traumatic events because the long-term nature of complex trauma does not allow the nervous system to recalibrate, instead leaving the body in a constant state of activation. Complex trauma is also called Complex Post-Traumatic Stress Disorder or C-PTSD.

Cultural appropriation - Yoga culture advocate Susanna Barkataki defines it this way:

Cultural appropriation is when someone uses someone else's culture, including practices, symbols, rituals, fashion, or other elements from a target or 'minority' culture, without considering the source, origins or people of that culture...Cultural appropriation happens when a dominant group adopts, benefits from, shares and even exploits the customs, practices, ideas, social and spiritual knowledge of another, usually target or subordinate, society or people.

Cultural appropriation clearly harms the source culture in a variety of ways:

1. Material harm

2. Disrespect or disregard to the values, practices, social, religious or cultural norms

Often that harm can span social institutions and political, economic, social, spiritual, cultural worlds.[110]

Cultural appropriation shows up in the world of healing when healers use modalities from other cultures without fully understanding the cultural context and/or without sharing power/material gain with the cultures who created the modality. Cultural appropriation can also look like cultural erasure. There are healing modalities from across Africa and the African diaspora, for example, that white healers are using without acknowledgement or understanding of the origins or cultural context.

Healing - Healing is a process. In the context of this book, personal healing refers to healing holistically, and primarily in mind, soul, and spirit. It is my belief that every individual should define what healing looks and feels like for them. Healing is also dynamic—what you want from it and what it wants from you will grow and change overtime. If you are someone with chronic pain and illness, your first healing milestone might be to really accept a diagnosis or physical limitations. It might also look like getting to a certain level of physical ability. Healing is not curing, but does sometimes involve curing an ailment or putting a disease into remission.

Kyriarchy - Kyriarchy is a term coined by radical feminist theologian Elisabeth Schussler Fiorenza to describe, as one of her students Lisa Factora-Borchers put it, "The human tendency for everyone trying to take the role of lord/master within a pyramid." It encompasses all the

---

110 Susanna Barkataki, "What Is the Difference between Cultural Appropriation and Cultural Appreciation?," November 14, 2020, https://www.susannabarkataki.com/post/what-is-the-difference-between-cultural-appropriation-and-cultural-appreciation.

intersecting structures of domination that humans use to rule over and oppress other humans such as capitalism, colonialism, patriarchy, and white supremacy, among others.

Medical Industrial Complex - Healing justice practitioners Cara Page, Susan Raffo, and Anjali Taneja write that "The medical industrial complex emerged as an extension of policing and state violence to control the biology and healing practices and to define the line between 'normal' and not."[111]

Neurodivergent - From Dr. Nick Walker:
Neurodivergent, sometimes abbreviated as ND, means having a brain that functions in ways that diverge significantly from the dominant societal standards of 'normal.'

Neurodivergent is quite a broad term. Neurodivergence (the state of being neurodivergent) can be largely or entirely genetic and innate, or it can be largely or entirely produced by brain-altering experience, or some combination of the two (autism and dyslexia are examples of innate forms of neurodivergence, while alterations in brain functioning caused by such things as trauma, long-term meditation practice, or heavy usage of psychedelic drugs are examples of forms of neurodivergence produced through experience).

A person whose neurocognitive functioning diverges from dominant societal norms in multiple ways – for instance, a person who is Autistic, dyslexic, and epileptic – can be described as multiply neurodivergent.[112]

111 Susan Raffo, "Healing Histories: Disrupting the Medical Industrial Complex," February 10, 2020, https://www.susanraffo.com/blog/healing-histories-disrupting-the-medical-industrial-complex-1.

112 Nick Walker, "Neurodiversity: Some Basic Terms & Definitions," NEUROQUEER, July 19, 2022, https://neuroqueer.com/neurodiversity-terms-and-definitions/.

Oppression - From dictionary.com: "Prolonged cruel or unjust treatment or control, the state of being subject to unjust treatment or control, mental pressure or distress." Oppression can be ideological, institutional, or interpersonal. It is useful in the healing process to observe when and how we have internalized oppression. An example of internalized oppression is believing that because you are disabled you do not have the same worth as an able-bodied person.

Patriarchy - The late feminist scholar and cultural critic bell hooks defines patriarchy as "a political-social system that insists that males are inherently dominating, superior to everything and everyone deemed weak, especially females, and endowed with the right to dominate and rule over the weak and to maintain that dominance through various forms of psychological terrorism and violence."[113] This system is evident in our epidemic of gender-based and sexual violence, lack of reproductive freedom for people with uteruses, the gender pay gap, and the male bias in medical studies, etc.

Racism - The institutional, structural, social, and systemic discrimination of people based on their race or ethnic group. In *How to Be An Antiracist*, author Ibram X. Kendi defines race as "A power construct of collected or merged difference that lives socially."[114]

Racial Capitalism - Racial capitalism is an economic system that subsists on the perpetual accumulation of capital and an increasing rate of said accumulation,[115] and depends on inequality that exists between humans based on race. It is dependent on slavery, violence, imperialism, and genocide.[116] I use the term "racial capitalism" to talk

113 bell hooks, "Understanding Patriarchy," accessed February 6, 2023, https://imaginenoborders.org/pdf/zines/UnderstandingPatriarchy.pdf.

114 Ibram X. Kendi, How to Be an Antiracist (New York, NY: One World, 2019).

115 "Racial Capitalism," Wikipedia, January 4, 2023, https://en.wikipedia.org/wiki/Racial_capitalism.

116 Robin D. G. Kelley, "What Did Cedric Robinson Mean by Racial Capitalism?," Boston Review, November 14, 2022, http://bostonreview.net/race/robin-d-g-kelley-what-did-cedric-robinson-mean-racial-capitalism.

about the specific ways our society has been set up to accumulate capital for white people by oppressing Black and Indigenous people.

Spoonie - A spoonie is someone with chronic physical and/or mental illness. The term "spoonie" grew out of a blog post titled "Spoon Theory" by lupus survivor and early chronic illness blogger Christine Miserandino. In trying to explain to her friend what it was like to have a chronic illness while they ate together in a diner, she likened her limited energy to having only a certain number of spoons each day. An able-bodied person might come into any given day with 12 spoons worth of energy, while someone with chronic illness might come into the day with six. If they want to do the laundry, that takes two spoons. Then they have to be very judicious about how they use their remaining four spoons. If they want to eat for example, preparing food might take the rest of their spoons, leaving no spoons for working, going to the store, visiting with a friend, or doing anything else.

Transgender - Denoting or relating to a person whose gender identity does not correspond with the sex they were assigned at birth. Sometimes I will simply use "trans" to denote a transgender person.

White Supremacy - When I write about white supremacy, I'm not simply referring to the belief that white people are genetically superior and should have dominance over people of other races. As Vann R. Newkirk II wrote in an October 2017 piece in *The Atlantic* titled, "The Language of White Supremacy,"[117] such narrow definitions of the term have historically allowed white men in suits to enact racist policies while public attention has been on other white people committing hate crimes. White supremacy is something that lives in all of us, regardless of our race. It also exists in our institutions, and in every facet of our

117 Vann R. Newkirk II, "What Is White Supremacy?," The Atlantic, August 2, 2021, https://www.theatlantic.com/politics/archive/2017/10/the-language-of-white-supremacy/542148/.

culture in the United States. In the essay, "What is white supremacy?" Elizabeth 'Betita' Martinez uses this definition from the Challenging White Supremacy Workshop, San Francisco, CA:[118]

> White Supremacy is a historically based, institutionally per-petuated system of exploitation and oppression of continents, nations, and peoples of color by white peoples and nations of the European continent, for the purpose of maintaining and defending a system of wealth, power, and privilege.

118Elizabeth 'Betita' Martinez, "What Is White Supremacy?" (Catalyst Project, n.d.), https://www.pym.org/annu-al-sessions/wp-content/uploads/sites/7/2017/06/What_Is_White_Supremacy_Martinez.pdf.

APPENDIX

More on Polyvagal Theory

This section provides a more technical explanation of Polyvagal Theory than what is offered in Section 1, Make Friends With Your Nervous System. Additional resources are listed at the end of this section.

The nervous system includes the brain, brainstem, cranial nerves, spinal cord, spinal nerves, and the enteric nerves, which govern the gastrointestinal tract. The Autonomic Nervous System (ANS) is composed of elements of the brain stem, some of the cranial nerves, and some parts of the spinal nerves. One of the major players is called the vagus nerve (vagus is Latin for "wandering") because of the way it wanders through the body, from the brainstem into the chest and abdomen, regulating many bodily functions including digestion, respiration, circulation, and elimination. Resmaa Menakem, somatic therapist and author of *My Grandmother's Hands: Racialized Trauma and the Pathway to Mending Our Hearts and Bodies,*[119] calls the vagus nerve "the soul nerve" because it is also responsible for how we experience "a felt sense

---

119 Resmaa Menakem, My Grandmother's Hands: Racialized Trauma and the Pathway to Mending Our Hearts and Bodies (London: Penguin Books, 2021).

of love, compassion, fear, grief, dread, sadness, loneliness, hope, empathy, anxiety, caring, disgust, despair, and many other things that make us human." The vagus nerve also assists in preventing inflammation, reducing pain, managing fear, and lifting your mood, among other things. The vagus nerve has two branches. The ventral vagal branch is the newer branch that developed in mammals, and it controls social engagement and our ability to relate to others. The dorsal vagal branch is the more primitive branch that controls immobilization behaviors, like animals feigning death and the human response to "freeze" in a stressful or frightening situation. All animals have the dorsal vagal nerve, including fish.

According to Polyvagal Theory, there are three neural circuits of the ANS that regulate our bodily functions to help us maintain homeostasis. These three circuits regulate our organ function as well as our emotional states, which in turn influence our behavior. These include:

- The ventral branch of the vagus nerve which regulates social engagement and positive states of relaxation;
- The spinal sympathetic chain, which regulates our fight or flight response; and
- The dorsal vagal branch of the vagus nerve, which regulates slowdown, shutdown, and depressive behavior.

The dorsal and ventral vagal branches, which govern the shutdown/collapse and social engagement responses make up the Parasympathetic Nervous System. The spinal sympathetic chain which governs the fight and flight responses makes up the Sympathetic Nervous System. As I mention in Section 1, Stephen Porges coined the term "neuroception" to describe how the neural circuits distinguish whether a situation is dangerous, threatening, or safe.

Here are some more details on the three primary physiological states that occur in response to neuroception:

1. Social Engagement (also called the ventral vagal) is regulated by the ventral branch of the vagus nerve and four other cranial nerves. It is the state we're in when our nervous system perceives safety and engaging with others feels desirable. This physiological state promotes rest and restoration, which allows for a level of physical and emotional health needed for friendship, loving relationships, mutual support, and collaboration. We can think of this state as "mobilization without fear." I like to think of social engagement as our home base. It is normal to experience activation of the other physiological states but social engagement is what we want to come back to.

2. Fight or Flight (most commonly referred to as the sympathetic nervous system, as in the previous chart) is regulated by the spinal sympathetic chain. This state allows humans and other animals to fight or run away from a threat. We can think of this state as "mobilization with fear." In this state our heart rate increases, our liver dumps sugar into the bloodstream for a quick rush of energy, and our bronchioles dilate so we can breathe more easily. This response relates to emotions of anger or fear.

3. Shutdown/Collapse (also called dorsal vagal) is regulated by the dorsal branch of the vagus nerve. This state is what allows an animal to play dead and arises from neuroception of mortal threat or death. It can be characterized as "immobilization with fear." In this state, the body seeks to conserve energy, our blood pressure drops, muscle loses its tone, and we might faint or go into a state of shock. The associated feelings are apathy manifesting as withdrawal or shutdown, helplessness, and hopelessness.

Freeze is a state that occurs between fight/flight and shutdown/collapse. This can be described as a felt sensation of "I need to do these things but I can't," or "I should do these things but I can't."[120] Two additional hybrid states include:

1. Play, friendly competition, or "mobilization without fear," combines activation of the spinal sympathetic chain and the ventral vagal social engagement circuit; and
2. Stillness, intimacy/intimate behavior, or "immobilization without fear," involves activity in both the ventral branch and dorsal branch of the vagus nerve. It is characterized by trusting, calm feelings, and allows us to be still and snuggle with someone, for example.

The three circuits of the ANS are hierarchical, with a step-like progression from one state to the next, in accordance with their evolutionary development. This predictable progression is often described as a ladder, like in the following visual. The bottom of the ladder is the dorsal vagal state, our oldest evolutionary response to threats, which triggers shutdown/collapse, or immobilization with fear. The next rung up the ladder is the fight/flight response or mobilization with fear, courtesy of the sympathetic chain. Social engagement, which comes from our most recently evolved circuit (including the ventral vagal branch) is at the top of the ladder. The hybrid states are depicted as Play, Stillness, and Freeze.

You might take a moment here to pause and tune in. Given the explanations of the different states and what you notice in your body right now, where might you be on the ladder at this moment? There is no right or wrong answer, this is just an opportunity to notice.

---

120 "Highest Self Podcast 447: How to Heal Your Nervous System - Your Guide to Somatic Healing with Sarah Baldwin," Sahara Rose, August 31, 2022, https://iamsahararose.com/single-post/highest-self-podcast-447-how-to-heal-your-nervous-system-your-guide-to-somatic-healing-with-sarah-baldwin/.

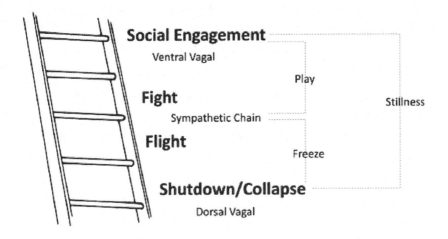

As I wrote about in Section 1, Step 1: Make Friends With Your Nervous System, making time to notice the state of your nervous system will support you in your healing. Over time you might also choose to experiment with manipulating your nervous system to put yourself in different physiological states.

Activating the spinal sympathetic chain circuit (fight/flight), inhibits dorsal vagal activity, interrupting the body's shutdown/collapse response. This is why exercise that stimulates fight/flight, like swimming or running, can help someone get out of a depressive dorsal vagal (shutdown/collapse) state. And you don't need to go one step up the ladder at a time. Increasing ventral vagal activity by spending time with loved ones, for example, can move a person from shutdown/collapse straight into social engagement, skipping fight/flight. In *Accessing the Healing Power of the Vagus Nerve: Self-Help Exercises for Anxiety, Depression, Trauma, and Autism,* author and bodyworker Stanley Rosenberg explains, "Activity in the ventral branch of the vagus nerve inhibits the two lower levels. Activation of the ventral vagal circuit... lifts us out of chronic activation of the spinal sympathetic system, and it also takes us out of dorsal states of shutdown."[121]

If you're new to even thinking about your nervous system, I recommend copying, printing, or drawing the ladder chart and hanging it up where you'll see it often (or ask someone to do this for you). The chart will serve as a visual reminder to check in with your nervous system regularly. The more awareness you cultivate, the easier it will be to take a pause and do one of the previous exercises. Once you have built some awareness of your own nervous system, you may start to observe when certain people, situations, or thoughts cause dysregulation or regulation in your system. I have noticed, for example, that every time I drive on a certain road that I like, I can feel my whole nervous system relax.

To learn more about Polyvagal Theory and how to work with it, I recommend:

- *Anchored: How to Befriend Your Nervous System Using Polyvagal Theory* by Deb Dana, LICSW
- *Accessing the Healing Power of the Vagus Nerve: Self-Help Exercises for Anxiety, Depression, Trauma, and Autism* by craniosacral therapist and Rolfer Stanley Rosenberg
- The Center for Body Up! Co-Regulation's videos and other resources on co-regulation at WeCoregulate.com. This is the work of Beth Dennison, MFT, MEd, LMT, SEP.

---

121 Stanley Rosenberg, Accessing the Healing Power of the Vagus Nerve: Self-Help Exercises for Anxiety, Depression, Trauma, and Autism (Berkeley, CA: North Atlantic Books, 2016).

Recommended Reading

In addition to the books I mention and recommend throughout the text, I wanted to highlight a few recent books with themes that strongly overlap with this one.

- *American Detox: The Myth of Wellness and How We Can Truly Heal*, Kerri Kelly (2022)
- *Inflamed: Deep Medicine and the Anatomy of Injustice*, Rupa Marya and Raj Patel (2021)
- *Liberated To the Bone: Histories. Bodies. Futures.*, Susan Raffo (2022)
- *Sacred Instructions: Indigenous Wisdom for Living Spirit-Based Change*, Sherri Mitchell (2018)
- *The Future Is Disabled: Prophecies, Love Notes and Mourning Songs*, Leah Lakshmi Piepzna-Samarasinha (2022)
- *The Invisible Kingdom: Reimagining Chronic Illness*, Meghan O'Rourke *(2022)*
- *The Myth of Normal: Trauma, Illness and Healing in a Toxic Culture*, Dr. Gabor Maté (2022)

How to Get in Touch

I can be reached through my website www.noellejanka.com/contact. Sign up for my email list to get free resources on personal and collective healing.

ACKNOWLEDGEMENTS

This book was made possible by a lot of really good music and the tremendous support of some really amazing humans, dogs, and ancestors. I'm especially grateful to my editor Claire Comiskey, and to Beth Ann Suggs, Jeremy Blanchard, and Suzanne Kingsbury for holding the publishing of this book as an inevitability. I am also grateful to my parents Les and Michele Janka for always cheering me on and repeatedly reminding me to focus on this book. Thank you to my brother for keeping me laughing, and for understanding the struggle of invisible illness when others didn't.

To the Gateless Writing community and my Gateless salon regulars, you inspire me. I'm grateful to Lindsay Wolff, Rada Yovovich, Heather Smith, Claire/Karl B. W. Müller, Samantha Cullen, Rachel Stevens, Rachel Riverwood, and everyone who gave me feedback on this book baby. Thank you to Sophia Breitag for the early enthusiasm and research support. Thank you to my colleagues at Harvard Kennedy School's Office of Career Advancement for keeping me smiling during a wild time and cheering me on in the latter half of birthing this book baby. Special thanks to my colleague Dr. Natascha Saunders for showing me what dedication looks like, and for sharing brilliant editing tips.

Thank you Alex Amorosi for your incredible wisdom and for getting me on the mat when I thought I was "done with yoga." Many thanks and gratitude to my yoga homes: JP Centre Yoga, Artemis Yoga, and Shelburne Falls Yoga. To my Western Mass friends, thank you for helping me slow down and showing me how little you need to live a really wonderful life. To Cloud Saddle Writers, thank you for introducing me to the magic of a good writing group, and for sharing your incredible writing, snacks, prompts, and feedback with me. To all my lovers, thank you for taking me on unforgettable accessible adventures, and loving me so well even in my worst moments. Special thanks to Joshua Breitner, Rafe Halsey, and Glen Moore for your support of this book-birthing process. Laura Richardson, Melanie Kowalski, and Kazmira Nedeau, you are my everything. Thank you for being the best, and for letting me whine and celebrate so many moments related to this book. Nettle, thank you for caring for me in all the ways, and knowing what I needed before I was brave enough to ask for it. You are a gem and I'm so freaking lucky to have you in my life. Jack Schultz, thank you for being on the healing path with me. You give the best hugs and you are a bright light to me and so many. Veronica Willette, thank you for keeping me laughing, flowing, grooving, and fed in some of my darkest days. Karen Nutt and George Kingsley, thank you for teaching me how to work hard and have a great time in the process. Everything you taught me has served me so much in my healing.

I am so grateful to all my mentors, teachers and healers, but especially Leslie Salmon Jones, Jeff Jones, Tanya Tarail, Rachel Marshall, David Vendetti, Ame Wren, Brenna Matthews, Daniel Max, Kathy Tarnoff, Tim Kelleher, Tommy Priester, Ishita Sharma, Mayer Kirkpatrick, Sandra Gray, Tricia Beretz, Dr. Mayra Cruz-Polanco, Dr. Janice Pegels, Marilyn Downs, Ann Horwitz, Anne Drogin, Chris Turcotte, all the chiropractors and front desk people at Arlington Chiropractic, Dr. Viet Le, Dr. Patrick Doody, Maude Evans, Kirsten Ackerman,

Zo Tobi, Susan Barney, Heather Smith, Katina Makris, Anna Adler, Marta Rodriguez, my peer counseling community, the Green Corps alumni network, and the ACE coaching community.

I am so thankful for all my healer and coach friends, and am eternally grateful to my spoonie buddies for keeping me sane and sharing so much wisdom with me, particularly A.M., Samantha Cullen, Eli Grobel, Sarah Regenspan, Riley Dwight, Emily Royce, David Curtiss, Kerry Ann Lang, Lindsay Wolff, and Heather Colman-McGill. I am also so grateful for the amazing beings whose work in the world contributed greatly to the soul of this book, especially Dr. Maria Nemeth, Pema Chödrön, Resmaa Menakem, Tada Hozumi, Dare Sohei, Kerri Kelly, adrienne maree brown, Lama Rod Owens, Rev. angel Kyodo williams, Leah Lakshmi Piepzna-Samarasinha, and so many unnamed parents of healing justice, disability justice, and queer liberation.

Many, many, many thanks to all my clients for lighting up my life and inspiring me to put this knowledge out into the world in book form. I appreciate ya.

Made in the USA
Coppell, TX
06 September 2023

21253617R00187